Early Wireless

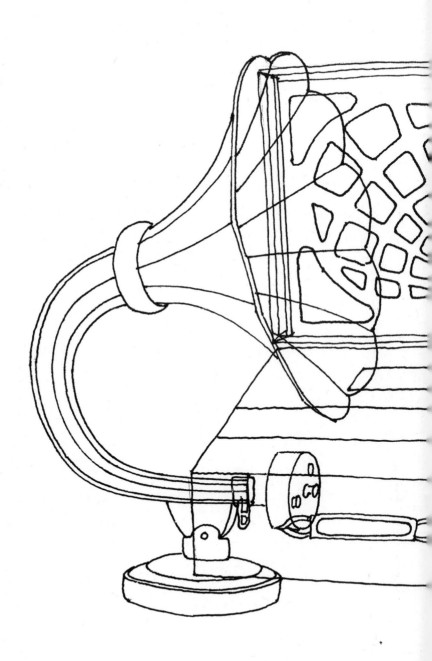

Early Wireless

ANTHONY CONSTABLE

MIDAS BOOKS

THE MIDAS
COLLECTORS' LIBRARY

General Editor: Brian Jewell

Smoothing Irons by Brian Jewell
Treen and Earthenware by Anne Forty
Veteran Talking Machines by Brian Jewell
Teapots and Coffee Pots by Philip Miller
Clock Types by E.J. Tyler
Motor Badges and Figureheads by Brian Jewell
Teapoys Chests and Caddies by Philip Miller

First published 1980 by
MIDAS BOOKS
12 Dene Way, Speldhurst
Tunbridge Wells, Kent TN3 0NX

© Anthony Constable 1980

ISBN 0 85936 125 X

Printed and bound in Great Britain by
R. J. Acford, Industrial Estate, Chichester, Sussex.

Contents

Acknowledgements

The author wishes to thank all those who have helped, directly or indirectly, in the task of producing this work. Very grateful thanks are due to several members of the British Vintage Wireless Society for allowing their equipment to be photographed. In particular, thanks are due to David Read, Bill Journeaux and Ian Higginbottom who between them own 69 of the receivers illustrated. Thanks are also due to the Antique Collectors' Club for allowing the reproduction of Figures 67, 81, 91, 103 and 160 which first appeared in an article by the author in 'Antique Collecting' Vol.10, No.10. February 1976. Figures 61, 63, 65, 68, 71, 87, 153-159 have been reproduced by kind permission of the Victoria and Albert Museum. These items appeared in 'The Wireless Show' held at the Victoria and Albert Museum in association with the British Vintage Wireless Society in the Autumn of 1977. The author is also grateful to the Science Museum, London for their kind permission to reproduce Figures 10, 13, 18 and 19. Thanks are due to *Wireless World* for Figures 34 and 145 and for extensive use of their *Buyers Guide* published in 1926. Special thanks are due to those members of the California Historical Radio Society who provided photographs of their equipment prompted by their fellow member, David Brodie. Their equipment is illustrated in Figures 108-124 and 161-167.

Although some of the photographs have come from other sources, most of them have been specially photographed for this book and the author extends his very special appreciation to the photographer David Baughan who undertook the task with great interest and a keen sense of professionalism.

It is not possible to list all the reference material used in writing this book but the author considers it absolutely necessary to refer in glowing terms to two recent works which stand out above all others for the major contributions they have made to the subject. These are: *Syntony and Spark.* by Hugh G.J. Aitken. Published by John Wiley & Sons in 1976. *Saga of the Vacuum Tube.* By Gerald F.J. Tyne. Published by Howard W. Sams & Co. Inc. in 1977.

The author is indebted to both of these authors who have provided ideas and source material without which his own book could not have been written.

Finally, the author wishes to thank his family and friends who have always shown a sustained interest in his indulgent pursuit of collecting and restoring old radio sets.

Foreword

Long distance radio communication has become an integral part of 20th-century life. Entertainment, information and propaganda from all parts of the world can be plucked from the space within our own homes with consummate ease at any time of the day or night. Precision information can be transmitted across millions of miles of the solar system from exploring satellites.

By contrast and in retrospect, the 19th century was a silent world; a world in which news travelled slowly and the notion of broadcast entertainment had not been conceived. Out of this silence, however, grew the profusion of ideas which became the theoretical and experimental foundation of the new technology of 20th-century radio communication.

Since the early 1920s, the general public have actively participated in the development of the communications industry by merely buying and using their radio receivers. Since those days, the wireless receiver has evolved from the simple crystal set and instrument panel receiver of the 1922 period, through the energy hungry multi-valve giants of the 1930s and 1940s to the miniaturised pocket size transistor sets we know today. For many years the wireless set played a dominant role in the home and had a profound effect on shaping the very fabric of 20th-century life. It has been my intention in writing this book to see the wireless set as the culmination of a long pre-history. Part 1 traces this pre-history from the earliest times until man's knowledge of electricity and magnetism became adequate to the task of transmitting and receiving intelligent signals over long distances without connecting wires.

Part 2 traces the development from the crude detection devices available at the turn of the century to the full realisation of the thermionic valve as the vital element capable of detecting, oscillating and amplifying. Part 3 commences at the end of the First World War and traces the development of radio from the dawn of the age of broadcasting up to the 1930s, by which time the radio set had achieved adult status and had worked its way deep into the heart of family life.

While I have concentrated mainly on developments in Great Britain, mention has also been made of many of the important contributions

8

made by pioneers in other parts of the world — Germany, France, and particularly North America.

Students of wireless history and collectors of wireless equipment will quickly detect those areas which are inadequately covered. I trust, however, that they will also be the first to realise the need to be selective in a work of this sort. The receivers discussed, illustrated and listed in this book only provide the merest glimpse into the exceedingly active industry that grew from the humblest origins in the early 1920s to a vast complex of material suppliers, manufacturers and retailers in the 1930s.

I apologise in advance for any mistakes which may have occurred but make no apologies whatsoever for the thousands of omissions which, for the most part, were entirely calculated.

London 1979   A.C.

I Electromagnetic ripples: from Earliest Times to c1900

When, towards the end of the 19th century, Guglielmo Marconi and other enterprising visionaries began to appreciate the practical possibilities of communication over long distances without connecting wires, a new age had indeed begun.

It would be wrong to assume, however, that Marconi's early experiments in *wire-less* telegraphy were in themselves a great scientific innovation. Nothing new was invented for the occasion; the possibility of wireless telegraphy had already been amply demonstrated by Oliver Lodge and others and the eventual possibilities had been foreseen with remarkable clarity by William Crookes in 1892.

Marconi's experiments are of great historical importance, however, and will be considered in more detail later, but in the meantime it might be better to start exploring the origins of wireless telegraphy from the point of view of William Crookes' article in *The Fortnightly Review* in February 1892, almost exactly four years before Marconi came to England. Crookes was well known for his speculative, visionary thought. He was no 'science fiction' writer, however, and normally based his speculative thinking on sound scientific knowledge and a strong belief that science should have practical contributions to make and, where possible, should be used to earn money.

The title of Crookes' article was 'Some Possibilities of Electricity' and contained a good deal of discussion on electromagnetic waves. He referred to the work of Oliver Lodge and Heinrich Hertz as increasing our understanding of the vastness of the electromagnetic spectrum of which the optical portion was merely the visible tip of a huge unexplored continent. Crookes went on to refer to those portions of the spectrum with wave-lengths of thousands of miles down to a few feet and to speculate on the possibilities of using them for transmitting and receiving intelligence. 'Rays of light,' he went on to say, 'will not pierce through a wall, nor, as we know only too well, through a London fog. But the electrical vibrations of a yard or more in wavelength of which I have spoken will easily pierce such mediums, which to them will be transparent. Here, then, is revealed the bewildering possibility of telegraphy without wires, posts, cables, or any of our present costly appliances. Granted a few reasonable postulates, the whole thing comes well within the realms of possible fulfilment.'

William Crookes showed that he appreciated the full extent of existing knowledge. He realised that it was already possible to generate waves of any desired wavelength, to radiate them in any direction and, with a suitable detector, to receive them at a distance, and he stated that morse signals could thereby be passed from one operator to another. He thought that it was now only necessary to achieve more delicate means of detection and to improve and simplify existing devices for generating waves of specific desired length. Most importantly he recognised the need to develop detecting devices that would respond to wavelengths between certain defined limits and be silent to all others.

His anticipation of the tuned wireless receiver of some years later is truly remarkable as can be seen from the following passage: 'I assume here that the progress of discovery would give instruments capable of adjustment by turning a screw or altering the length of a wire, so as to become receptive of wavelengths of any preconcerted length. Thus, when adjusted to fifty yards, the transmitter might emit, and the receiver respond to, rays varying between forty-five and fifty-five yards, and be silent to all others.'

There is some evidence to suggest that William Crookes' article had a catalytic action among scientists of the day who began to become less theoretically single-minded than hitherto. The bits of hardware required for a wire-less signalling system began to appear and be used for demonstration purposes (Oliver Lodge), for Naval signalling experiments (Captain Henry Jackson), as a storm indicating device (Alexander Popov in Russia) and indeed as a practical signalling device by the young Marconi in Italy.

Thus the year 1892 might be thought of as the year of the awakening. The long sleep and the gentle dreaming were now over and a short period of dawn would follow before the sun-rise... before Marconi would burst upon the world with the necessary degree of technical knowledge, commercial skill and sheer practical vision to bring into being the communications revolution that was the consequence of his successful commercial exploitation of his own experiments with wireless telegraphy.

In our enthusiasm for the truly remarkable events following this 'dawn' and 'sunrise' period it is all too easy to forget the 'dreaming' and even the 'sleep-walking' that preceded the awakening. The coming of wireless was not achieved in a moment of inspiration. Many events

11

simply had to occur and many discoveries had to be made before it could even be contemplated in the manner of William Crookes' *Fortnightly Review* article. It is only possible to consider very briefly the exciting pre-history of wireless in this book for, in any depth, it would become a dominant theme.

Electricity, we all know, is a word that was coined from the Greek word for 'amber' by Dr William Gilbert, court physician to Queen Elizabeth I. The electrical properties acquired by amber when rubbed with a piece of cloth had been observed (though not investigated) by the Greeks as long ago as 600 BC. Magnetism was also known to the Greeks and, possibly much earlier, to the Chinese. The connection between magnetism and electricity was occasionally observed when, for example, a ship's compass would become demagnetised or even reverse magnetised when the ship was struck by lightening. This and similar observations were made during the early part of the 18th century but it was not until the year 1820 that controlled experimental evidence of the connection was provided by the Danish physicist, Hans Christian Oersted. He showed that an electric current (i.e. moving electric charges) could cause a nearby compass needle to be deflected (Fig.1). Michael Faraday, in about 1831, showed that moving magnets could produce electric currents (Fig.2), the principle of the electric dynamo. He had previously shown that changes of current in one circuit could be detected as current changes in an adjacent circuit, the principle of the transformer. These effects are called 'electromagnetic induction' and, in the latter form, became the basis of the first method of aerial wire-less telegraphy. Although these effects constitute physical 'action at a distance', Faraday made a significant contribution to 19th century thinking by choosing to think in terms of the intervening space being filled with electric and magnetic *fields*. This may only seem like a minor variation in the choice of words, but to those scientists gifted with the ability to think deeply about the fundamentals of nature, it meant all the difference in the world.

Although Faraday was undoubtedly one of the great scientific geniuses of the 19th century he had insufficient mathematical ability to develop a theoretical structure for his new ideas. It was James Clerk Maxwell in about 1865 who took on this important task with complete success. Considering Faraday's 'fields' in space as existing in their own right, Maxwell came up with his comprehensive electromagnetic theory. He expressed the two symmetrical ideas, (i) Changing electric fields produce magnetic fields and, (ii) changing magnetic fields produce electric fields, in a precise mathematical form known, and still used today, as Maxwell's

12

Equations. The incredible thing about Maxwell's Equations is that, when applied in free empty space, they take on the form of a wave motion propagating itself freely from place to place at the speed of light. Maxwell proposed that light itself was electromagnetic in origin and that waves of every possible wavelength could in principle be generated by varying the electric currents that could be produced with batteries or magnets.

Experimental verification of Maxwell's ideas was undertaken eventually by Heinrich Hertz in Germany who, in 1887, finally succeeded in generating and detecting electromagnetic waves (Fig.3) and to demonstrate that they had all the properties of light waves — they obeyed the laws of reflection, refraction and polarisation. Thus wireless waves had now arrived and were, as a result of Hertz's very thorough and scientific work, fully accepted by the scientific community.

However, some years prior to Hertz's discovery, Professor David E. Hughes discovered, early in 1879 (Maxwell died in Dec. 1879) all the essential features of wireless telegraphy with a spark transmitter and a microphonic detector. Unfortunately, Professor Hughes did not carry out systematic scientific experiments and his demonstrations were not accepted by his scientific colleagues as being anything more remarkable than the then well known Faraday induction effects. In fact, it is now known that Hughes was really on the right track and had anticipated both Hertz and Lodge in achieving successful propagation of signals by the very waves predicted by Maxwell some 15 years earlier. Hughes later claimed to have transmitted up to 500yds along Gt Portland Street using a clockwork spark transmitter and needle-coke detector (Fig.4). David Hughes was a professor of music but took a great interest in telegraphy and invented a printing telegraph in 1855 and the carbon microphone in 1878. His experiments with electromagnetic radiation were rather intuitive and he probably knew nothing about Maxwell's predictions. He realised the importance of his findings, however, and demonstrated them to a delegation of prominent members of the Royal Society at his home at 94, Gt Portland Street.

The learned members of the Royal Society were not overly impressed with Hughes' demonstrations and Professor Stokes stated that they could be explained by well known electromagnetic induction effects anyway. Hughes was greatly discouraged and did not publish his results. The first time that the world became aware of Hughes' investigations was nearly 20 years later. William Crookes, however, in his *Fortnightly Review* article, referred cryptically to Hughes when he said that he himself had participated in actual transmission of messages over short distances, 'from one part of a house to another without intervening wire'. Indeed Crookes was referring to Hughes' house in Gt Portland Street, barely 150yds from the site later to become Broadcasting House (Fig.5).

Later, when writing about his work, Prof. Hughes referred to the masterly researches of Hertz but pointed out that his own microphone or coherer detector was much more sensitive than the one Hertz used. It is difficult to say what Hughes *could* have done *if* things had been different though it is really quite certain that Hughes could never have undertaken the experimental verification of Maxwell's equations in the manner so admirably accomplished by Heinrich Hertz several years later. Publication of Hughes' findings might have given rise to considerable interest in the scientific community and resulted in the earlier discovery of the coherer detector. Hughes' experience cannot be rated as a great scientific event but it could be remembered as an example of a great missed opportunity.

A coherer is a sensitive detector of electromagnetic radiation and consists of a glass tube of metal filings with metal plugs at the ends of the tube (Fig.6). In this form, it was essentially introduced in 1890 by Edouard Branly of the Catholic University of Paris. The electrical resistance between the ends of the tube is normally very high but when excited by an applied voltage and particularly by waves generated by a spark coil, the resistance drops considerably. The resistance remains low until the coherer is 'restored' by giving it a little jolt. Thus the coherer acts as a sort of latching switch and can be made to actuate electrical devices either directly or by way of a relay when heavier currents are needed. An electric bell can thus be sounded when the electromagnetic waves from a distant spark cause the resistance of the coherer to drop (Fig.7). Of course, because the coherer is a *latching* switch, it remains 'on' once it has responded. But if the hammer on the electric bell is allowed to gently jolt the coherer then the coherer returns to its high resistance state immediately. In this way the bell will sound for just as long as sparks are radiated and it will stop as soon as the sparks stop. Short bursts of sparks and long bursts will result in the dots and dashes of the morse code sounding at the receiver end by the electric bell.

Although more sensitive than the simple resonant wire loop and spark gap used by Hertz, the coherer was still a very unreliable device. But in the mid 1890s it was the detector used by most of the experimenters of the day. Captain Henry Jackson and Oliver Lodge were using them in England, Alexander Popov had one in Russia, Braun and Slaby in Germany, Calzecchi Onesti and the young Marconi in Italy. All were using systems similar to the one devised and demonstrated by Oliver

14

Lodge in the lectures he gave during 1894: at the Royal Institution in London in June, at a 'Ladies Conversazione' of the Royal Society also in June and at the British Association meetings at Oxford in August.

Lodge later claimed that the Royal Society lecture was the first public demonstration of wireless telegraphy. He also claimed that morse signals had been sent during the Oxford lecture from the spark transmitter at the Clarendon Laboratory to the lecture theatre of the Oxford Museum, a distance of about 180ft. If these claims are true then Lodge must undoubtedly be credited with the world's first demonstration of wireless telegraphy and, although doubt has been expressed in some quarters, there are probably good reasons to believe in Lodge's claims. One strong reason is that Dr Alexander Muirhead, after hearing Lodge give his June lecture at the Royal Institution, called Lodge's attention to the commercial possibilities almost immediately. Muirhead repeated some of Lodge's experiments himself and later collaborated with Lodge in the commercial exploitation of wireless telegraphy. The Lodge-Muirhead system achieved some success in the early 1900's as one of the early commercial systems. It is very possible that Lodge did in fact turn his attention to telegraphy applications of Hertzian waves after being prompted by Muirhead, and in time for both his 'Ladies' Evening' and the British Association lecture in August. Up to this time, Lodge was undoubtedly at the forefront of the scientific and technical advances that could at any moment have become converted into the full commercial exploitation of wireless telegraphy. But this was not to be the case although Muirhead, in associating himself with Lodge, brought into existence the link between his own conventional *wired* telegraphy expertise and the new science of Hertzian waves. It was just this link that so far seemed to have been missing. And yet, even when it took place, nothing very startling happened. The pair of them could have embarked upon a career as meteoric as Marconi's of a couple of years later. But their pace was leisurely. Lodge was, after all, a scientist and to him the important achievements were to pursue the theoretical work of Clerk Maxwell and to continue to refine the experimental work of Heinrich Hertz.

Conventional *wired* telegraphy was at this time a highly developed technology and the Post Office held statutory monopoly over land telegraphy in Britain. The cable companies operated overseas links and terminal stations employing sensitive relays, sophisticated switch gear and a host of signalling devices. There was here a whole technology on to which, at any moment, the new science could become grafted. Despite all the activity, publications and public lectures that occurred in the field of embryonic wireless telegraphy the 'accident of history' had yet to occur which would link successfully the Hertzian wave experiments with the established systems of communication. The not very commercial Lodge-Muirhead link was scientific and technical and moved slowly. It somehow lacked the commercial and entrepreneural spirit that history was waiting for.

Wireless telegraphy as such, but in no way connected with Hertzian waves, had for some time been working itself into a blind alley with Mr. William Preece, the Chief Engineer to the Post Office. But blind alleys always look blinder in the light of experience and hindsight. Preece had been experimenting since 1884 with telegraphy without wires using the principles of Faraday's laws of electromagnetic induction. From even earlier, March 1882, he had shown an interest in the possibilities of wireless telegraphy using conduction through water. He read a paper to the British Association in 1882 describing his successful transmission and reception of telegraphic signals across the Solent from Southampton to Newport when the cable had broken down. However, from 1884 onwards he pursued doggedly his interest in the inductive method. He set up and investigated several situations in which signals in one circuit were transmitted to receivers in another quite separate circuit some distance away. It became quite clear however, that as soon as the distance between the two circuits became greater than the lengths of the wires in the circuits the signal strength began to diminish considerably. Long wires parallel to one another and separated by comparatively short distances could produce very successful inductive transmissions. In 1884, for example, Preece found that messages were picked up from insulated wires buried in iron tubes in Gray's Inn Rd, London, by unconnected telephone circuits carried on poles over the roof tops of houses some 80ft high. He used this system with some success to communicate between ground level and pit bottom (360ft down) at Broomhill Colliery, and again across the Mersey at Liverpool, also between Shrewsbury and Much Wenlock and again in the Bristol Channel. The Bristol Channel experiments were particularly successful between Lavernock Point in Wales and the lighthouse on the small island of Flatholm 3.3 miles off shore. Communication to Steepholm, an island 5.35 miles off shore, was by no means as successful: there were perceptible signals, but conversation was not possible. When, in March 1895, the cable connecting the Island of Mull with the mainland broke, Preece maintained the ordinary service entirely by inductive methods.

This energetic interest of Preece in a form of wire-less telegraphy emphasises the fact that there was a recognised need for wire-less

16

communication as well as some achievement in that direction. And he was by no means the only person to be involved in this sort of work. It is all the more surprising therefore that the Hertzian system that now existed did not find an immediate role in establishing links across channels and with off shore lighthouses. Preece undoubtedly wanted such a system and realised the shortcoming of his own which, in requiring wires at each station as long or longer than the intervening distance, was not really saving on wires and presented great problems on small islands! If Preece wanted an efficient compact system and Lodge had it, why didn't they get together? The fact is they didn't, and so history was written.

In January 1894, Heinrich Hertz died and Augusto Righi, Professor of Physics at Bologna University wrote a memorial paper (or obituary) in which he described the brilliant experiments of Hertz in some detail. The 20 year old Guglielmo Marconi used to spend the summer months at his parents' estate, the Villa Grifone, outside Bologna where Professor Righi was a neighbour and family friend. Marconi had inadequate qualifications to enter the University of Bologna but Righi allowed him to 'audit' his classes and to use his laboratories in the pursuit of his interests in physics and chemistry and particularly in anything to do with electricity. Marconi became very interested in the idea of applying Hertz's waves to telegraphy from about this time. He may have been influenced by Righi himself. Righi had a great interest in Hertzian phenomena and was an authority on the subject of extremely short waves in the region of 10cm wavelength — the microwave region. Working in close proximity to Righi must have given Marconi many opportunities to become familiar with the scientific literature published by other authors. And Marconi, whose mother was Irish/Scots was quite familiar with the English language and would very probably have read some of the work of Oliver Lodge. Not being a 'matriculated' student at the University, he was free to pursue his interests as he pleased without the straight-jacket of pending examinations and such like. He was soon producing and improving Lodge coherers and went to work in his attic along lines very similar to those being demonstrated by Lodge in England.

After two years of experimenting, Marconi had a very reliable system capable of transmitting signals over some distance. To Marconi, it seems, distance counted above all else. Directional effects and tuning to particular wavelengths were of no immediate interest to him. He was like the novice tennis player who concentrates on really hitting the ball before he begins to worry about direction and strategy. This was his strong point — his single-minded interest in distance. Even if Lodge had wanted

17

to achieve distance, he could not have been single-minded about it as he already knew too much about directional effects and particularly about 'tuning'. Marconi, on the other hand, probably knew nothing about tuning at all and therefore could not be distracted by it. Every improvement he made was directed towards achieving greater distance. He empirically found that if he raised his antenna or aerial as high as possible and at the same time introduced a connection to earth at both the transmitter and receiver, even greater distances could be achieved.

Marconi attempted to exploit his apparatus and offered the Italian Government a demonstration in the autumn of 1895. The Italian Government was not interested.

So, at the age of 21, Marconi and his mother set sail for England where they arrived in February 1896. Marconi's mother, Annie, had many relatives in England. As Annie Jameson, she was a member of the well known Irish-Scottish family of whisky fame, and had eloped in 1864 to marry Giuseppe Marconi, a silk merchant widower some 17 years her senior. She had visited England briefly on several occasions since, and it appears that she brought Guglielmo on at least one of these occasions and that, at the age of five, he attended private school in England for perhaps a couple of years.

On arriving in England, Annie and Guglielmo were met by Henry Jameson Davis (Annie's cousin) who arranged lodgings for them at 77 Hereford Rd., Bayswater, London. There remains a bit of a mystery about Hereford Rd., as the number 101 appears in Marconi's handwriting on one of his visiting cards.

It may, in retrospect, seem very sensible for the Marconi's to have set sail for England where there was a lot of scientific interest in Hertzian waves. It was also the centre of international trade and it was the world's foremost naval power. Communication between ships at sea was a matter of the greatest importance and as soon as wireless telegraphy got under way this would become a top priority application. From December 1895 Captain Henry Jackson of HMS Definance had been carrying out experiments on the wireless transmission of morse signals aboard the HMS Defiance, the Naval Torpedo School at Devonport. Jackson had suggested the use of Hertzian waves for naval communications as early as 1891. During 1896 he successfully transmitted and detected morse signals aboard the Defiance.

However, despite all the logical reasons why England might have been thought the country of choice, the Marconi's went there for more simple and practical reasons. Annie's relations lived there, she and her son would have no language difficulty there, the Jameson family was

18

reasonably wealthy and could be relied upon for all the other forms of support and encouragement as well. Henry Jameson Davis was himself in practice as an engineer and sought the advice of an electrical engineering friend A.A. Campbell Swinton. Campbell Swinton wrote a letter of introduction for Guglielmo to William Preece, the Engineer-in-Chief at the Post Office. The latter is dated 30 March 1896 and simply states that "... a young Italian of the name of Marconi (has the idea of) ... a new system of telegraphy without wires. It appears to be based on Hertzian waves, and Oliver Lodge's coherer, but from what he tells me he appears to have got considerably beyond what I believe other people have done in this line. ... I also think that what he has done will very likely be of interest to you. Hoping that I am not troubling you too much".

On the advice of Jameson Davis, Marconi began drawing up a provisional patent specification and on 2 June 1896 filed the world's first patent for using Hertzian waves for a system of wireless telegraphy under the title: 'Improvements in Transmitting Electrical Impulses and Signals and in Apparatus therefor.' The first diagram from this patent can be seen in Fig.8.

What did Marconi really offer to the world at this stage? A great invention? Not really, all the devices he used were well known to many people and were well described in many publications. But he did offer an 'improved' system. His coherer was certainly an improvement on previous types and his aerial system did use raised antennae and grounded plates at both the transmitting and the receiving end. Such aerial systems were nothing new but Marconi did realise that they could increase the effective distance over which transmissions could be usefully sent if he installed them on both the transmitter and the receiver. His system, although it included nothing new, brought together a number of useful existing ideas and bits of hardware and constituted the first practical compact system specifically designed for wire-less communication. His complete patent specification was not accepted until 2 July 1897 and in it Marconi really takes possession of a lot of other peoples' ideas which, when all's said and done, were really hanging about waiting for just such an opportunist. Marconi offerred the world the missing ingredients — a single-minded interest in the use of Hertzian waves for long-distance wireless telegraphy, a belief in the commercial possibilities, a well designed compact system as opposed to a collection of various bits and pieces, certain definite practical improvements over existing systems, a dogged determination and a whole family structure prepared to assist in every way.

However, even before the provisional specification was filed in June 1896, Marconi had met William Preece and demonstrated his apparatus satisfactorily to him. Preece as it turns out, could not have been better chosen. Here was a man who himself had been experimenting for years with wire-less telegraphy using Faraday's electromagnetic induction as the working principle. He was convinced of the need for a good wire-less system and recognised the limitations of his own methods. The blind alley along which he had for so long been travelling suddenly opened up in the person of Marconi. Marconi didn't arrive on the doorstep and say he had an *idea* and proceed to say how Lodge's coherer and Popov's aerial and Hertz's oscillator etc etc *could* be made to work. Not at all, he came with a complete set of working apparatus which he switched on in the General Post Office Building and it worked.

In no time at all Marconi had Preece convinced of the merits of the Hertzian wave system of transmission and reception of telegraphic signals and many experiments were carried out to achieve greater and greater distances. The first formal demonstration was given to the Post Office in July 1896 over a distance of a few hundred metres between the roof tops of two nearby Post Office buildings. In September, Marconi demonstrated his signalling method to the Post Office officials on Salisbury Plain over a distance of about 1.75 miles using parabolic reflectors at the transmitter and receiver. Marconi and Captain Jackson had met each other the day before the Salisbury Plain tests to compare notes... as both naval and army representatives were present at the demonstrations. Later experiments on Salisbury Plain in March 1897 covered a distance of over four miles. Preece returned to his old experimental ground in the Bristol Channel and in May 1897 Marconi was able to signal right across the channel from Lavernock Point to Brean Down. In November 1897, transmissions took place from the Needles, Alum Bay, Isle of Wight and Madeira House, Bournemouth. Marconi then returned to Italy for demonstrations over the 18km between Spezia and the cruiser San Martino.

On the 20 July 1897, while Marconi was away in Italy, 'The Wireless Telegraph and Signal Company Ltd.' came into existence with Jameson Davis as its first Managing Director. This was the world's first company devoted entirely to manufacturing wireless equipment. Its formation marked the end of one era and the opening of the next. In 1900 it was re-named 'Marconi's Wireless Telegraph Company.'

Wireless telegraphy was now here to stay and was to become a serious commercial enterprise with a fighting world of marketing competition, patent litigation and international involvements lying not too far ahead.

The press, or as we might now say, the media, had taken very favourably to Marconi and so had the public generally. He was fêted as the inventor of wireless wherever he went and was later to become known as 'Marconi the Mastermind' and was even to receive a share in a Nobel prize for physics. But despite all the sycophantic hullabaloo surrounding the name of Marconi, contributions were made by him that could not be, or at least were not, made by anybody else. He brought such qualities to the world as were required to close one era and open another.

F1762

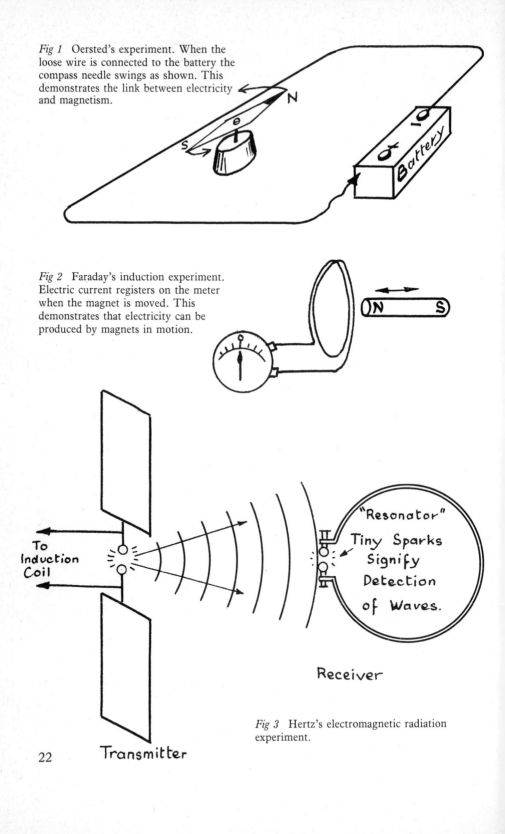

Fig 1 Oersted's experiment. When the loose wire is connected to the battery the compass needle swings as shown. This demonstrates the link between electricity and magnetism.

Fig 2 Faraday's induction experiment. Electric current registers on the meter when the magnet is moved. This demonstrates that electricity can be produced by magnets in motion.

"Resonator"
Tiny Sparks
Signify
Detection
of Waves.

To
Induction
Coil

Receiver

Fig 3 Hertz's electromagnetic radiation experiment.

Transmitter

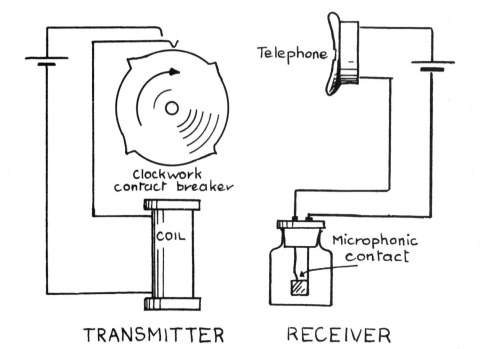

TRANSMITTER   RECEIVER

Fig 4 David Hughes' experiment. The Inductive sparks at the transmitter generated electromagnetic radiation later called Hertzian waves. The 'microphone detector' was of the 'bad contact' or coherer type. Different forms of detector were used, one of which consisted of a piece of coke carbon and a steel spring.

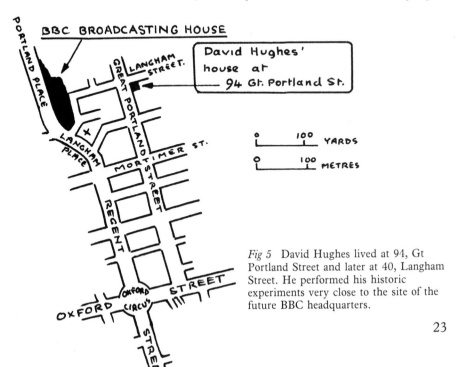

Fig 5 David Hughes lived at 94, Gt Portland Street and later at 40, Langham Street. He performed his historic experiments very close to the site of the future BBC headquarters.

23

Fig 6 A Branly coherer tube.

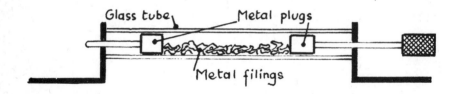

Glass tube   Metal plugs

Metal filings

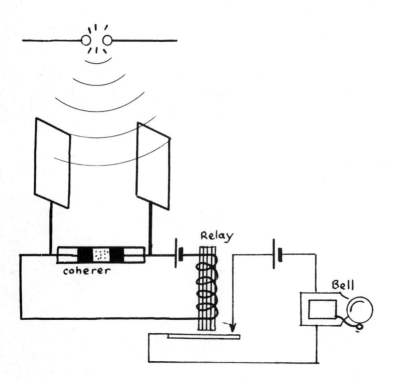

Relay

coherer

Bell

Fig 7 Coherer and sensitive relay
arrangement for actuating a bell circuit.

Fig 8 Taken from the first diagram in
Marconi's patent No.12039 — the
world's first radio patent.

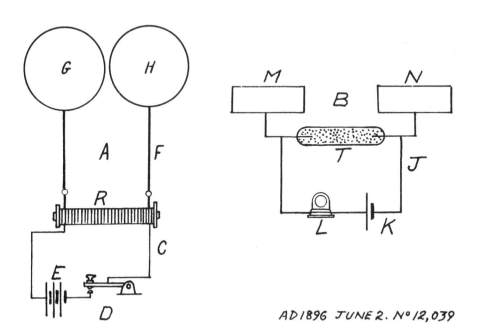

AD 1896 JUNE 2. Nº 12,039

II From Coherers to Valves: From 1897 to World War I

Although wireless telegraphy was now a reality, it still had a big struggle ahead to demonstrate its reliability over other means of communication. Its place was not easy to establish in those days. Little thought had yet been given to its possible use for voice transmission and the notions of entertainment and broadcasting did not seem to have been entertained by even the wildest dreamers.

Between 1897 and the first world war, the general public only caught glimpses of what was going on from the frequent press announcements. They took no direct part in those early developments which aimed at improving sensitivity, range and selectivity. The most obvious applications were to achieve good communications at sea between ships, to establish links across large expanses of water and to provide a new means of military intelligence.

The fascinating events which took place in those early days can be read about in various works but, for our purposes, only a small selection need be considered in order to examine the route taken by the new technology as it advanced into the twentieth century.

COHERER DETECTORS

The early Branly coherer detectors used by Marconi and others came in various forms but most consisted, as previously mentioned, of metal filings between two metal plugs in a glass tube.

The Italian Navy Coherer developed by P. Castelli and Lieutenant Solari consisted of a small glass tube with two iron or steel plugs. A small drop of mercury was held between the plugs. This coherer, unlike the Branley coherer, required no jolt to decoher it... it is a so-called 'self-restoring coherer' (Fig 9).

The Lodge-Muirhead Coherer (Fig 10) was also self-restoring and consisted of a small wheel with a sharp edge just touching a small pool of mercury as it revolved by clockwork. The mercury had a thin film of oil on its surface and the wheel was thus normally insulated from the mercury by this oil. When a signal of sufficient strength was received, the oil film broke and contact was established with the mercury. At the completion of the signal, the rotating wheel ensured automatic switching off again (decohering) and the detector was then ready for the next signal. The manner in which the coherer was originally used in a receiving circuit is shown in the accompanying diagram (Fig 11) of Marconi's apparatus which is adapted from an article written for The Electrician, June 11th 1897 by William Preece.

Coherers were inherently insensitive devices and had the added disadvantage that they were easily triggered by unwanted effects such as mechanical vibration or nearby electrical disturbances. The voltage at which they triggered was also rather variable and, for signalling purposes, they were very slow acting. Nevertheless, the early days of wireless telegraphy relied wholly on the various forms of this primitive detector. In December 1901, Marconi received signals in Newfoundland from Poldhu in Cornwall using a coherer. The type of coherer he used seems to have been the so-called Italian Navy self-restoring type. Also, the coherer was not arranged, as in Fig 11 so as to actuate a relay and electric bell. It was connected directly to a sensitive telephone ear piece making the whole arrangement very similar to the crystal sets which came a few years later.

SYNTONY

Early spark transmitters generated a wide range of wavelengths rather than the narrow bands required for good selectivity. Similarly, receivers were unselective and responded to any transmitted signal that happened to be strong enough. The chaos that can result from such untuned circuits was of course realised from the earliest times. The practical aspects came to light in 1899, for example, when Marconi was trying to secure a contract to supply the United States Navy with wireless equipment. From the U.S. Navy's historian we read the sarcastic comment, '. . . the interference was perfect.' Later, at the international yacht races in 1901, the Associated Press and the Publisher's Press Association hired Marconi and the Wireless Telegraph Company of America respectively for reporting the event. The American Wireless Telephone & Telegraph Company also took part making three transmissions trying to operate at the same time. The overall effect was a disaster although it has been stated that some boisterous rivalry was taking place. . . one of the American teams generating some of the longest dashes ever heard!

Some form of tuning was obviously necessary. This required the use of coils and condensers (capacitors) and when these components had the same physical dimensions in both transmiters and receivers 'syntony' would result. Syntony was the word used by Oliver Lodge to mean resonance or sympathetic vibrations and meant simply that the transmitter would radiate most of its power at a certain well defined wavelength and the receiver could be tuned to respond best at that wavelength. Now, Marconi had already by 1898 introduced a transformer (pat No 12326 App. 1 Jan. 1898) into his coherer circuit (Fig 12) consisting of two coils of wire, one in the aerial circuit and the other, the secondary, in the coherer cirucit. This transformer was also used in transmitter circuits and was called a 'jigger'. Such transformers must have their two windings and associated circuitry in resonance, i.e. well tuned, if they are to function efficiently as devices which transfer energy from one circuit to the next.

The original reason for using a transformer had nothing to do with tuning, however. It was first used in order to take the high resistance, voltage actuated coherer away from the grounded end of the aerial where the voltage was at a minimum, a so-called voltage anti-node. It seems that Professor Slaby understood this point immediately he saw Marconi's demonstration on Salisbury Plain and solved it by using a syntonic side wire or feedline which took the coherer to a part of the aerial circuit where the voltage was a maximum, a so-called voltage node. The two solutions to the problem were equally good but Marconi's had the advantage that an aerial transformer demands to be tuned, and thus Marconi was guided to the notion of syntony. Many of his first experimental transformers didn't work at all and they only became useful devices when it was realised that the primary and secondary circuits had to be properly matched.

Marconi added fixed condensers to his circuit both to give some degree of tuning and also to provide a reservoir capacitance for the very variable capacitance of the coherer. He patented the transformer in Britain and the United States. The British patent (No 7777) was filed on 26 August 1900, accepted 13 April 1901 and became known as the four sevens patent. The US patent (No 763,772) was filed on 10 November 1900 but was not issued till 28 June 1904.

Oliver Lodge probably knew more about the theory of syntony, tuning circuits of every variety, than any other living scientist. He had, furthermore, already taken out a patent (No. 11575) in 1897 with the title: 'Improvements in Syntonized Telegraphy.' Application for this patent was filed on 10 May 1897 nearly eight weeks before Marconi's original patent referred to in Part 1 was accepted and became 'public'. Lodge's patent was for a complete system of wireless telegraphy but, unlike Marconi's, Lodge's was specifically designed to transmit and to receive electrical oscillations of 'a particular frequency.'

Without syntony, wireless telegraphy could never have advanced very far. Today, we take tuning for granted. Vast numbers of powerful transmitters can operate throughout the world, each pumping out its energy at a very precisely defined frequency. Our radio sets are capable of tuning to particular stations in a very precise way and we do not expect interference from other stations. In 1897 Lodge understood the importance of tuning and the whole structure of his patent showed this. Marconi, on the other hand, had at first attached little importance to tuning but by 1898 he had stumbled across the idea as a by-product of his aerial transformer.

Other investigators were well versed in the matter of syntony, notably Professor Ferdinand Braun in Germany and Nikola Tesla in the United States. Lodge's 1897 patent was of the utmost importance in establishing for legal purposes, the origins of the tuned circuit in wireless telegraphy. Marconi paid no royalties to Lodge for manufacturing equipment which, although based on the Marconi 7777 patent, derived ultimately from the Lodge patent. Much bitterness grew up between the two men and between the Marconi Company and the Lodge-Muirhead Syndicate. It was not until 21 October 1911 that the two sides were brought together (by William Preece) with a successful compromise solution. The Lodge-Muirhead syndicate was dissolved, Lodge's patents were purchased by the Marconi Co. for an undisclosed amount, Lodge received a 'stipend' of £1000 per annum for the remaining life of the patent (another 7 years) and he accepted a position, nominal at least, as scientific adviser to the Marconi Company.

Thus tuning systems came to be a fundamental part of all wireless telegraphy equipment. Coils of wire and capacitors came in various forms both fixed and variable. One of the best known commercial products of the period was the Marconi multiple tuner (Fig 13). The electrical circuit of this device is shown in Fig 14. The multiple tuner was first developed in about 1904 by C.S. Franklin of the Marconi Company and it was patented in 1907. It was capable of tuning a receiver circuit over the four wave-bands, 80—150 metres, 150—1600 metres, 1600—2000 metres and 2000—2600 metres. The multiple tuner was employed extensively as a part of the receiving equipment used aboard ship and was normally operated in conjunction with another famous device, the magnetic detector. The coherer detector, with its inherent

29

lack of reliability, was replaced in the early years of the twentieth century by other forms of detector.

THE MAGNETIC DETECTOR AND RECTIFIERS

The earliest coherer detectors were simply sensitive electrical switches and were switched from the 'off' condition to the 'on' condition by incoming signals. Other principles of detection also became known and the effect of electromagnetic radiation on ferro-magnetic materials was one of them. As early as 1842, Joseph Henry of Princeton University had observed that magnetised needles became demagnetised when in the vicinity of discharging Leyden jars. In 1895, Ernest Rutherford used the principle to detect Hertzian waves over a distance of three quarters of a mile at the Cavendish Laboratory in Cambridge. Figure 15 shows the arrangement used by Rutherford in which a sensitive magnetometer (an instrument for measuring magnetic fields) changed its deflection when a pulse of electromagnetic radiation arrived at the receiving aerial.

Later modifications to this equipment were made by Professor Ernest Wilson in 1897 and by Marconi in 1902. A final version of the magnetic detector, patented in 1902, consisted of an endless band of soft iron wires moving through a pair of coils situated close to a couple of permanent magnets (Fig 16). This form of detector was still not very sensitive, but it was extremely reliable and was particularly good for use at sea where conditions could be anything but favourable. Unlike many other contemporary devices, it required no delicate readjustments and it could be used with headphones to continuously listen for incoming signals. It was in world wide use for many years and became familiarly known as the 'Maggie'. Unlike the coherer detector, which is a voltage operated device, the Maggie is a low impedance current operated detector. It was normally used in conjunction with the multiple tuner and was connected up as shown in Fig 17.

The most important feature of the magnetic detector had nothing to do with any possible increase in sensitivity it might have had over the coherer. The signals detected by the Maggie were heard in head-phones and did not have the slowing-up mechanism of the decohering tapper which so hampered the coherer. The coherer could only be used to send telegraphic morse signals at a very low speed — considerably slower than for conventional wired telegraphy. The magnetic detector, on the other hand, allowed good high speed morse to be detected and brought wireless telegraphy more into line with conventional cable communication links ... and hence made it more competitive.

The magnetic detector came into widespread use from 1903. It does not rectify the incoming signal as we have since become used to with diodes of every description. The magnetic detector does however have a slight rectifying action but this is only a second order effect so that, while it can even today be used to detect voice transmissions, its sensitivity is far below that of the true rectifiers which followed closely on its heels.

The first true rectifier used for the detection of Hertzian waves was the diode valve invented by Dr. John Ambrose Fleming in 1904 (Patent No. 24850, filed 16, Nov 1904). Fleming, it appears, was afflicted with mild deafness that was worsening and existing detectors were difficult for him to use. He therefore searched about for some device which would give him a visual indication of the received signals with good sensitivity. He had been experimenting since 1882 with the so-called 'Edison Effect' whereby current flowed only one way between the filament and a plate inserted in an ordinary electric light bulb. With slight modifications to the circuits he had previously used he soon found that it was possible to observe the detected signals on a galvanometer connected in series with one of his Edison bulbs and he quickly patented the device.

Rectification itself, or the non-linear characteristics of certain natural crystals was nothing new and had been the subject of experiments for thirty years. Ferdinand Braun had, he later claimed, used crystals for electromagnetic detection in 1901. But crystal detectors did not arrive on the scene properly until 1906.

Fleming correctly interpreted the action of his diode valve in terms of rectification and most radio frequency detectors since that date have relied on this principle. An early form of the Fleming valve is illustrated in Fig 18 and one of the receivers manufactured by the Marconi Co. in which a later version of this valve was used is illustrated in Fig 19.

Crystal detectors (Fig 20) appeared in 1906. Ferdinand Braun patented his psilomelan (a hydrated oxide of manganese) detector on 18 February 1906 and General H.H.C. Dunwoody patented his carborundum detector one month later in the USA. But L.W. Austen filed his British patent for a tellurium-silicon detector only three days after Braun's application in Germany. Greenleaf W. Pickard filed his patent for a silicon-metal rectifier in August 1906 though claimed to have been working on such detectors since 1902. All this activity makes the year 1906 truly the year of the crystal. Crystal detectors are voltage sensitive devices and are normally connected as shown in Fig 21. When a crystal and metal are used the metal was often in the form of a thin copper wire called a 'cat's whisker'. When two crystals were used in contact with each other, the detector was called a 'Perikon detector'. When carborundum was used, it normally had a flat steel spring in pressure contact with it and it was normally biased with a battery and potentiometer as shown in Fig 22. The reason for this bias was purely empirical in that the forward characteristic of the steel-carborundum junction became more sensitive when used in this way.

Crystal detectors came into widespread public use many years later when broadcasting began. Although they could not amplify incoming signals, they were generally simple to use, required no batteries, and had a much better tonal 'fidelity' than most of the valve devices that were in use in the early 1920's. When used today, crystal detectors are remarkably reliable devices and once adjusted can retain their sensitivity for many days without re-adjustment. However, in 1906, the principal form of transmitter generated electromagnetic waves by producing a violent spark. When a crystal detector comes anywhere near to such a transmitter it promptly ceases to function until it is reset ... a problem that persisted into the 1920's. On board ship, this problem could be even more acute. When the operator had finished listening, he then pounded out his own message from his own spark transmitter after which he had to re-adjust his crystal before he could again begin listening. The magnetic detector had no such defect. Provided that the flat steel spring of the carborundum detector was sufficiently pressurised, this effect was also not so noticeable with this form of detector. The carborundum detector and various forms of Perikon detector were the commonly used ones for Naval and military use. The so-called cat's whisker detector had few applications before it came into widespread domestic use in the 1920's. Used with a galena crystal (lead sulphide) the cat's whisker detector is very sensitive and the frequent re-adjustments that were often necessary were well tolerated by the many users in the 1920's who, in any case, were unable to afford anything more elaborate.

FURTHER ADDITIONS TO THE FLEMING VALVE

The Fleming Oscillation Valve as it was called was of fundamental importance to the development of wireless telegraphy because it introduced the notion of rectification for detection purposes. Subsequently, the terms rectification, detection and de-modulation were to be used almost simultaneously albeit a little carelessly. However, to improve matters all round some form of amplification was necessary.

Dr. Lee de Forest in the United States had been working on various applications of wireless telegraphy since his student days at Yale University in the late 1890's. He made several attempts to devise more sensitive detectors than those already in existence and his several patents

32

show clearly that he was developing ideas along incandescent and thermionic principles. He acquired a Fleming valve in 1905 and had some duplicates made by H.W. McCandless & Co. of New York. Towards the end of 1906 de Forest asked the same company to make some valves with a 'gridiron' shaped wire between the filament and plate. A few days after de Forest had this valve made he was forced to resign from his position as vice-president and scientific director of the American de Forest Wireless Telegraph Company because of legal and financial trouble. He was given $1000 severance pay, half of which went in lawyers' fees. The various forms of Audion (as he called his valve) for which he now had patents pending, he also took with him, as his backers considered them worthless anyway. His new 'grid type' of audion was first tested by John V.L. Hogan, a high school boy acquaintance, on 31 December 1906. De Forest filed a patent on 29 January 1907 and it was issued on 18 February 1908 as US patent number 879532. This three electrode Audion, or triode, as it came to be known universally, was capable of not only detecting a signal by the process of rectification, it was also capable of amplifying.

The de Forest triode Audion continued to be made by the McCandless company up to 1915 and during this time it was used with only a slowly growing appreciation of its potentialities. Up to about 1912, it was used mainly as a simple detector. Any amplification that may occasionally have been achieved was very erratic, partly because the people using them did not fully understand their working characteristics and partly because the McCandless company were not making them to any very definite specification. The electrodes were made by hand and varied considerably from valve to valve and the vacuum produced inside the glass bulb was in no way quality controlled. Thus each Audion produced had its own special characteristics and any amplification achieved was more a matter of luck than the result of sound knowledge.

However, in 1912, Dr. Harold D. Arnold of Western Electric recognised the possibilities of the de Forest Audion. At this time triode valves being produced in the USA and elsewhere were all essentially soft valves, i.e. there was a lot of residual gas left in the valve. Furthermore, even during the life of one valve, this was a very variable quantity, the gas pressure could rise as more gas was released from the internal surfaces or the pressure could drop as the gases present became adsorbed on internal surfaces. Valves were very unstable and difficult to use. When amplification was achieved it could sometimes be very large owing to the presence of curious kinks in the characteristic curves of these valves. Slight alterations in signal strength or in anode voltage could result in 'blue glow', a phenomenon which most people brought up on even the most modern valves have experienced as the valve goes soft. Yet valves went on being produced with gas in them because most people seemed to believe that it was necessary. Dr. Arnold recognised that the presence of gas was a liability, that with it, it was an 'ionic' device and without the gas it could become an 'electronic' device.

Arnold produced a valve with a good high vacuum (a so-called 'hard' valve) and with a Wehnelt, or oxide coated, filament. After several development problems had been solved in connection with producing a sufficiently good vacuum, a sufficiently robust electrode assembly and a sufficiently good oxide-coated filament, trials began. Finally, on 18th October 1913, Arnold's high-vacuum triode came into use at Philadelphia as an amplifier in a telephone repeater circuit.

Arnold's high vacuum triode was undoubtedly the first successful use of the triode as an amplifier with sufficient reliability and ease of use to ensure the future of high vacuum valves for commercial exploitation.

In Britain at this time, about 1913 but probably starting earlier, H.J. Round of the Marconi Company devised a soft triode with an oxide-coated filament and a special side tube or top-tube containing a bit of asbestos (Fig 23). This asbestos could be heated to increase the gas pressure in the tube and so alter the characteristics of the valve at will. The Round valve was perhaps a bit tricky to use, but in experienced hands it could produce great amplification. The asbestos tube was usually heated with matches and, as P.P. Eckersley remarked in his lecture to the BBC Engineering Society in 1960, the conscientious operator finished up with fingers like sausages-burnt ... He also said that matches always worked better than the various heating coils that were devised!

In Germany, Robert von Lieben, Eugen Reisz and Sigmund Strauss developed for Telefunken the magnificent looking so-called LRS relay, a soft triode. This was patented on 15 October 1912 and was eventually claimed to be capable of an amplification factor of 33 with a useful life of 1000—3000 hours. This valve also had a side tube containing an amalgam of mercury for the purpose of adjusting, by local heating, the condition of the vacuum inside the valve. The Lieben-Reisz valve, or the Liebenröhre, as it was variously known, was manufactured by AEG-Telefunken and by the Siemens & Halske companies. It was still in use at the outbreak of the First World War when research began which quickly lead to the development of high-vacuum valves.

In France, there was little interest in the triode until early 1914 when Colonel Gustav Ferrié was visited by one Paul Pichon, an erstwhile

34

deserter from the French army. Pichon had worked in Germany at the Telefunken Company, and was in the United States at the outbreak of war. He returned first to England where Godfrey Isaacs the Managing Director of the Marconi Company, advised him to return to France despite being a deserter. Pichon was arrested when he arrived at Calais, but he requested an interview with Commandant Ferrié whom he knew and during their meeting produced several de Forest Audions and associated paper work acquired while in America. Ferrié conscripted Pichon and assigned him to military radio service. Ferrié himself had obtained a three Audion amplifier before the war through his associate Emile Girardeau as a result of seeing one when he was in the USA visiting, among others, Reginald A. Fessenden, one of North America's celebrated radio pioneers. He had put this amplifier away and forgotten about it! Showing Pichon's 'trophies' to Girardeau brought it to light again.

No time was lost in getting valve production under way. The EC & A Grammont company in Lyon produced them under their trade mark FOTOS and, later, the Compagnie Générale des Lampes at Ivry began production. The Grammont valves were designated TM Fotos and the Compagnie Générale valves were designated TM Metal, the 'TM' signifying Télégraphie Militaire. They were high-vacuum valves and had better operating characteristics than most available valves during the First World War. The design was particularly simple (Fig 24) and the base-pin configuration became the standard throughout Europe in the post-war years. Pichon's timely arrival in France resulted in the highly successful development of a valve manufacturing industry and gave to the allies a plentiful supply of valves that had undoubtedly better performance characteristics than those available in Germany.

The French valve was much used by the British in the First World War and became very popular as the 'R' valve after the war and well into the broadcasting era.

Although the French valve became of great importance to the Allies during the First World War, other valves were also available. The Round valve was itself in use in the Marconi type 27 receiver. There were also, for example, the White valve (Fig 25), the Navy's Osram R2A (Fig 26). The Air Force C valve (Fig 27) and The Marconi V24 (Fig 28). These few valves are very representative of what was available during the First World War but, of course, there were others. Not all of the valves were available throughout the war. The Air Force C valve, for instance, was not introduced until September 1918. The V24 was introduced by the Marconi Company (by Captain Round) in 1916. This valve was developed for use as a high frequency amplifier. The filament leads come out at the end caps and the grid and anode come out at opposite sides. The purpose of this was to keep the interelectrode capacity down to an absolute minimum because, when used for high frequency operation, the inter-electrode capacity acts as a 'feed-back loop' as shown in Fig 29. When a signal is fed back in this way, it tends to have an additive effect on the signal arriving at the grid and causes the valve to become very unstable in operation. It is rather like putting a microphone too near to a loudspeaker — most readers will have experienced the resulting screech when this is done.

THE VALVE AS AN OSCILLATOR

This idea, that the energy coming out of an amplifying device can be fed back in to the in-put side is called positive feed-back. If positive feed-back occurs when it is not required it is the most troublesome thing. But, on the other hand, it gives rise to one of the most important applications of the triode — and one which, so far in this narrative, has not been mentioned. It is the ability of the triode valve to function as an oscillator.

In the circuit shown in Fig 30, the inductance and capacitance L and C considered together have a certain natural frequency. That is, if a voltage is applied to C, it will discharge into the coil and momentarily appear as a magnetic field. But then the magnetic field will collapse and, in so doing discharge its energy back into the capacitor C. The cycle will then be repeated over and over again. The frequency at which this happens, the number of times per second, depends entirely on the dimensions of the coil and the dimensions of the capacitor. Or, to use the proper units, on how big the inductance is in, say, microhenries and how big the capacitance is in, say, microfarads. However, the energy cannot go back and forth indefinitely because the wires in the circuit have resistance and where there is resistance there will be heat produced and consequent loss of energy. So now, if this coil and capacitor are connected to the valve as shown, the small oscillations in the coil will be amplified by the valve and the larger oscillations appearing in the anode circuit can now be fed back to the original coil and, when conditions are just right, the energy being fed back will just balance that being lost and continuous oscillations will result.

Right from the earliest days of wireless, the need for a source of continuous oscillations was appreciated by several pioneer investigators. The spark transmitter used in the early days produced rapid bursts of damped high frequency oscillations. Continuous, undamped wave generators were developed by Valdemar Poulson (the arc transmitter)

36

from about 1903, and by Reginald Fessenden and E.F.W. Alexanderson (the high frequency alternator) between 1908 and 1915. Even the spark transmitter, in its most advanced form at the Clifden transmitter on the west coast of Ireland, had become something of a continuous wave generator by 1911. The generation of continuous waves was necessary for a number of reasons and probably, to the early engineers, the most important was again connected with syntony. A damped high frequency oscillation generator defeats the aims of resonant circuits by spreading its energy across too wide a band of frequencies. On the other hand, a continuous wave generator is a narrow band system and lends itself admirably to all the principles of good syntony — well designed resonant circuits would then result in transmitters causing minimum interference to other operators in the same wave-band.

Another reason for wanting continuous waves was recognised at a very early stage by the Canadian Reginald Fessenden working in the United States. He realised that continuous waves would be required for the transmission of voice signals rather than simply the dots and dashes of the morse code, i.e. for telephony rather than telegraphy. This idea of wireless telephony was of great importance to Reginald Fessenden long before it had even occurred to most people. He made his first rough attempts to transmit voice over the air on 23 December 1900 over a distance of one mile on Cobb Island. There is some evidence that the voices of Fessenden's men were heard across the Atlantic at his Machrihanish station in Scotland as early as November 1906! On 24 December 1906 Fessenden made what can only be considered as the first broadcast concert. He played the fiddle, sang Christmas carols and played Handel's Largo on the phonograph and announced: 'If anybody hears me, please write to Mr Fessenden at Brant Rock'. Ships' operators out in the Atlantic did hear him and some overcame their astonished disbelief and did write to tell him.

The equipment used by Fessenden consisted originally of a high interruption frequency spark generator (10,000 sparks per sec. later increased to 20,000). He used Mr Alexanderson's high frequency alternator for his later work and by 1908 this was capable of delivering 100,000 cycles at 2 kilowatts. Other workers were involved by this time in wireless telephony and in 1908 Professor Q. Majorana of Rome covered a distance of 270 miles. One difficulty of these early attempts lay in the fact that large currents had to be handled by the microphones. Majorana used a liquid microphone (Fig 31) that was capable of handling 10 amps at 50 volts, corresponding to a cool 500 watts! Actually many of those early microphones were anything but cool. There are tales of operators having their beards or noses singed. We can also read of systems having two microphones and a switch. When one microphone got too hot the second one could be switched into the circuit.

The introduction of the valve oscillator changed all this. Valves can oscillate and the oscillation energy can be amplified by other valves. The oscillation frequency can be extremely high e.g. 1,000,000 cycles per sec quite easily. The high frequency oscillations can then be modulated by microphones placed in very low current parts of the circuit. So when the valve was discovered to have this oscillating property, it was a great day indeed, and in a way, completed the story of the valve's arrival. When did this happen?

Well, like so many inventions, when the time was ripe it happened all over the place. The first patent was taken out by Alexander Meissner of Telefunken in Germany on 9 April 1913. This was closely followed by patents taken out in Britain (by C.S. Franklin of Marconi's) in June and in the USA by Major E. Armstrong in October, and again in Britain by H.J. Round of Marconi's in May 1914.

All these men employed essentially the same principle in their patents and had been working on them for some time before their patents were filed. The basic idea involved in all oscillating circuits such as in Fig 30 is called 'feed-back' and many circuits were developed which made use of the principle. It can also be used in a simple receiving circuit to boost the incoming signal. This system was used very widely and was called 'reaction' or regeneration. Most radio sets during the 1920's, before the days of the commercial development of the superheterodyne, employed reaction circuits similar to that described by Franklin in 1913. A typical single valve regenerative receiver circuit is shown in Fig 32.

During the First World War, every possible form of wireless equipment was brought into service and the valve underwent tremendous development at this time. Many companies began to manufacture valves, thus preparing themselves for the revolution that was to take place in the post-war years. All through the war years the older methods were used side by side with the newer technology. The introduction of successful high-vacuum valves did not put crystal sets out of business. One of the best known First World War wireless receivers was the Mk III tuner crystal receiver designed by the Marconi Wireless Telegraphy Co. Ltd. and is shown in Fig 33. The circuit details are shown in Fig 34.

The Mk III tuner was used by Air Force ground staff to listen to reports from reconnaisance pilots flying back and forth between the lines. The operator was normally underground in the vicinity of Battery

Headquarters. Information from 'sky-patrol' was fed to the gunners. A series of B's tapped out by a pilot was said to mean, 'finish your b. . .y breakfast and get on with the shooting.' and the signal CI (—•—• ••) was said to mean the pilot was going back to see the bar-orderly.

Although the Mk III tuner was only a crystal set, it had a well designed tuning circuit. This was quite necessary as the three flights in a given squadron, for example, would employ wavelengths of, say, 140, 180 and 220 metres. At the same time an adjacent squadron might be allotted the wavelengths 160, 200 and 240 metres. Operators were expected to be able to maintain contact with a particular plane despite all sorts of unfavourable conditions including jamming.

Towards the end of the war a Mk IV tuner was made. This was considerably smaller than the Mk III and not many of them were made. Fig 35 shows the only known surviving example of this set.

The First World War provides our second turning point in history. It ushered out the old era — the era of sparks, arcs, coherers, magnetic detectors and soft valves. It ushered in the age of the high-vacuum valve and provided the technological starting point from which a huge electronic industry could grow, based, as it would be for the next four and a half decades, on valves of every description.

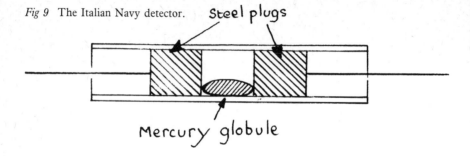

Fig 9 The Italian Navy detector.

Steel plugs

Mercury globule

Fig 10 The Lodge-Muirhead coherer.

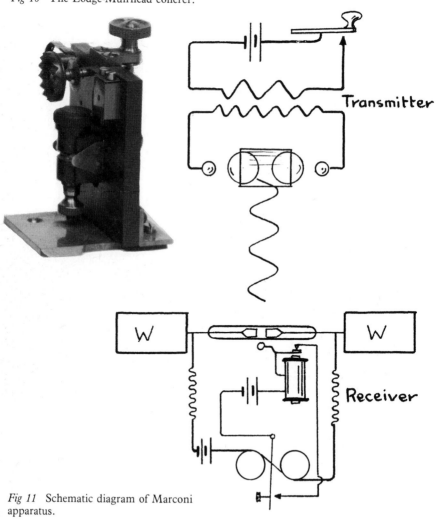

Transmitter

W   W

Receiver

Fig 11 Schematic diagram of Marconi apparatus.

Fig 12 Circuit arrangement of Marconi's aerial transformer or 'jigger'.

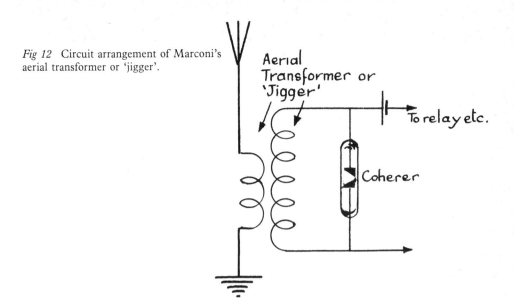

Fig 13 The Marconi multiple tuner.

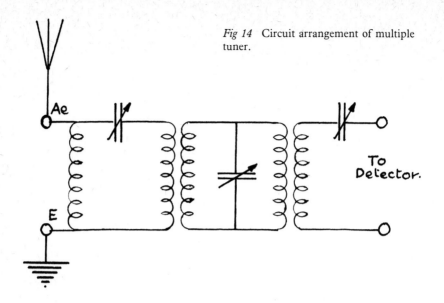

Fig 14 Circuit arrangement of multiple tuner.

Ae

E

To Detector.

Fig 15 Rutherford's experiment with magnetic detection.

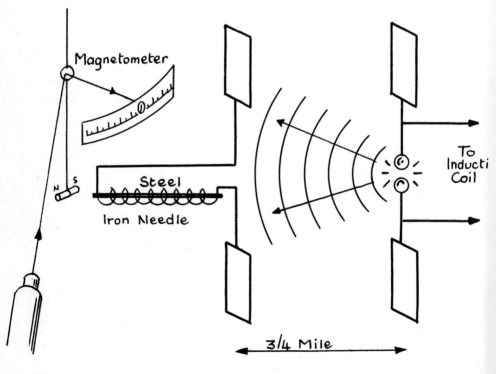

Magnetometer

N S

Steel

Iron Needle

To Inducti Coil

3/4 Mile

Fig 16 Marconi magnetic detector with lid in background.

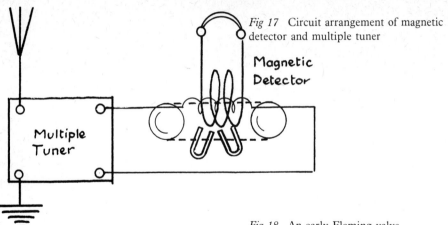

Fig 17 Circuit arrangement of magnetic detector and multiple tuner

Magnetic
Detector

Multiple
Tuner

Fig 18 An early Fleming valve.

Fig 19 An early Marconi set using two Fleming valves.

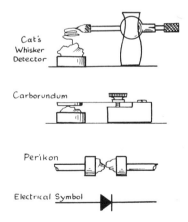

Fig 20 The three types of crystal detector.

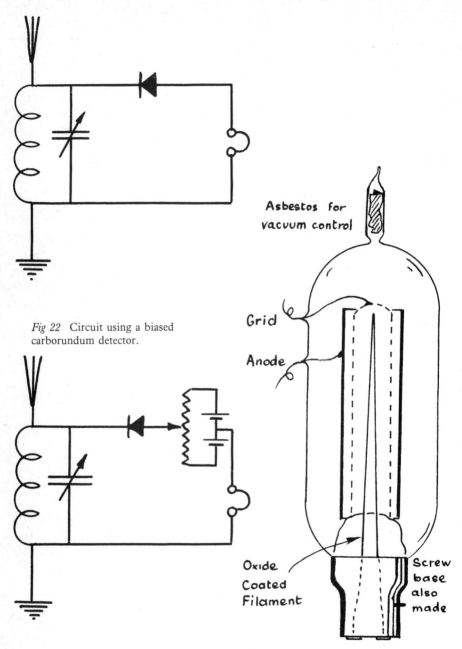

Fig 21 A simple crystal detector circuit.

Fig 22 Circuit using a biased carborundum detector.

Asbestos for vacuum control

Grid

Anode

Oxide Coated Filament

Screw base also made

Fig 23 H.J. Round's soft valve.

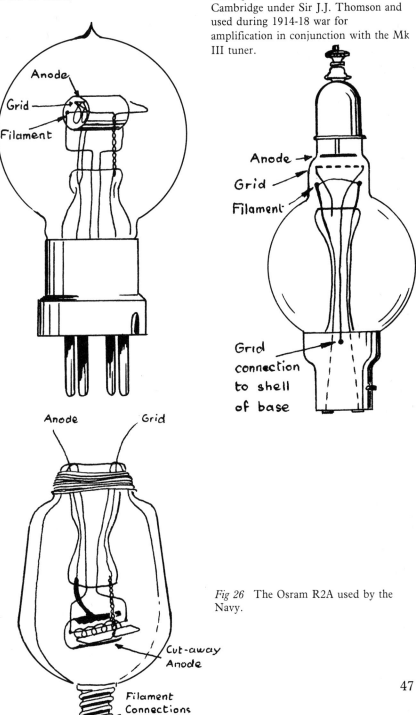

Fig 24 The 'French' valve. Known also as the 'R' valve.

Anode

Grid

Filament

Fig 25 G.W. White's soft valve developed from earlier work at Cambridge under Sir J.J. Thomson and used during 1914-18 war for amplification in conjunction with the Mk III tuner.

Anode →

Grid

Filament

Grid connection to shell of base

Anode

Grid

Cut-away Anode

Filament Connections

Fig 26 The Osram R2A used by the Navy.

47

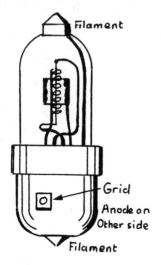

Fig 27 The Air Force 'C' valve. Design attributed to Captain S.R. Mullard.

Filament

Grid

Anode on Other side

Filament

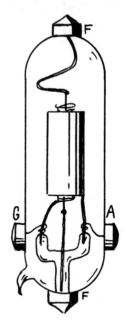

Fig 28 The V24. Designed by Captain H.J. Round for Marconi's.

F

G

A

F

Fig 29 The effect of grid-anode capacitance is to feed the valve output back to the grid. The instability caused by this effect is most notable at high frequencies.

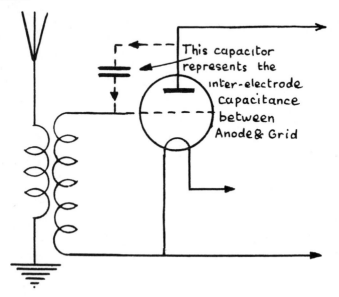

This capacitor represents the inter-electrode capacitance between Anode & Grid

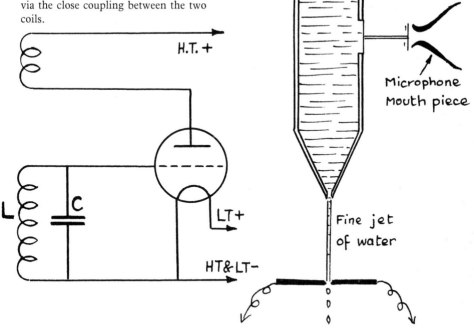

Fig 30 The natural oscillations set up in the L-C circuit are maintained by the valve which feeds back some of its output via the close coupling between the two coils.

H.T. +

L

C

LT+

HT&LT−

Fig 31 The principal of Pro. Majorama's liquid microphone of 1908.

Microphone
Mouth piece

Fine jet
of water

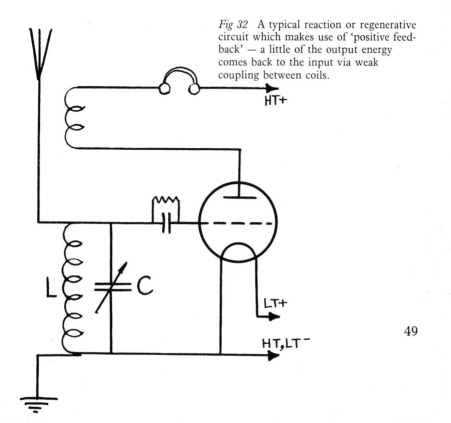

Fig 32 A typical reaction or regenerative circuit which makes use of 'positive feedback' — a little of the output energy comes back to the input via weak coupling between coils.

HT+

L

C

LT+

HT,LT−

49

Fig 33 A first world war Mk III tuner. Essentially a crystal set with very elaborate tuning circuitry and switching arrangements.

Fig 34 (right) The circuit of the Mk III tuner as published in 'Wireless World' in January 1920.

Fig 35 (right) The Mk IV tuner introduced towards the end of the First World War

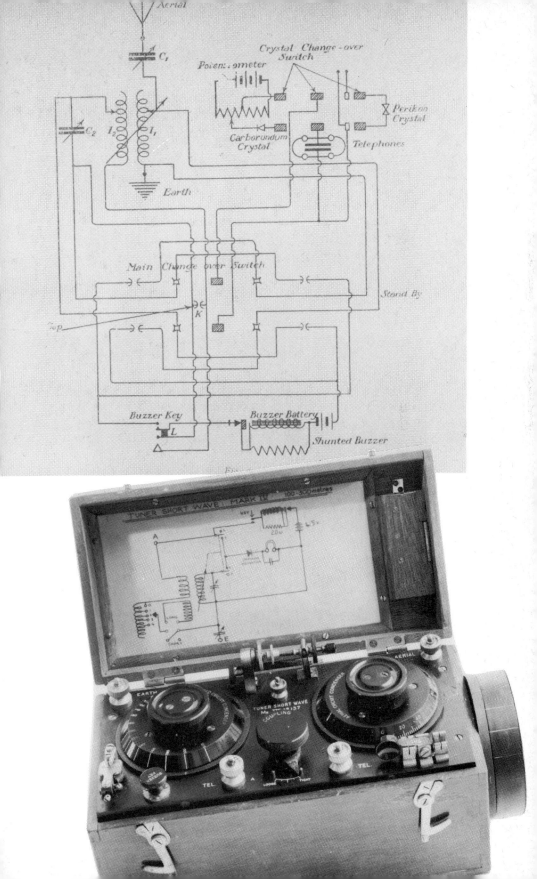

III Wireless Goes Public: From World War I to 1930

The many technical developments that took place during the First World War both in Europe and in the United States enabled, in principle, a flourishing new industry for providing wireless equipment of every description to grow up. However, in Britain, it took a long time before war-time restrictions were lifted. Amateur experimenters were very anxious to resume their pre-war activities and to extend them with the new technology of valve circuitry. Their experimental Post-Office Licences, issued before the war, were still legally in force. These were not cancelled until 5 July 1919.

The first signs of any relaxation in the Defence Regulations had come in April 1919 when manufacturers were notified that buzzers [sic!] could be sold without officially stating the use to which they were going to be put! Headphones and spark coils could be bought provided the purchaser signed a statement to the effect that he would not use them for sending or receiving messages by wireless telegraphy ... unless he obtained written permission from the Post Master General. On 21 October 1919, the Post Office announced that informal authority could now be obtained by people wishing to use receiving equipment. The use of valves was forbidden except where special permission was obtained from the PMG. A fee of ten shillings would be charged for the receiving licence.

From 23 February 1920, the Marconi Company operated a 15 kW transmitter at Chelmsford. This gave the few licence holders who owned the appropriate receiving equipment one of their first opportunities of hearing music and voice transmission in this country. However, a few months earlier, on 6 November 1919, a Mr Hanso Henricus a Idzerda began publishing a daily programme of his concerts from his transmitter in The Hague, Holland. These 'Dutch Concerts' became very famous and must have contributed a great deal to the desire among amateurs to get something like it operating in this country. A lot of interest was aroused when Dame Nellie Melba, the famous Australian soprano, took part in a *Daily Mail* organised concert from Chelmsford on 15 June 1920 on a wavelength of 2800 metres. This wavelength was sufficiently close to the 2600 metres used for regular time signals and weather reports from the Eiffel Tower transmitters to be heard by the large number of amateurs in Britain and Europe who had equipped themselves for the Paris transmission. By this time amateurs had begun to appreciate radio telephony for its home entertainment value and many began using telephony for their own transmissions. In the autumn of 1920, permission to 'broadcast' from Chelmsford was withdrawn owing to 'the considerable interference with other stations' as the Post Master General told the House of Commons on 23 November. On 14 February 1922, the Marconi Company's second broadcasting station began transmissions from Writtle near Chelmsford. The station had the call-sign 2MT and became well known as Two-Emma-Toc. The transmitter was originally 200 watts and operated on a wavelength of 700 metres. From 22 May 1922, it began transmitting on a wavelength of 400 metres in order to avoid interference from one of the harmonics of the GPO station at Leafield. Permission to establish a station had been granted to the Marconi Company following a petition signed by the presidents of sixty-three amateur societies asking for the reinstatement of professional transmissions in Britain and presented to the Rt Hon F.G. Kellaway, the Post Master General, on 29 December 1921.

When permission was granted it was a little 'reluctant' judging from the conditions to which it was subject: 1) Power not to exceed 250 watts; 2) Transmission time not to exceed one half-hour per week; 3) The station must close down for three minutes in every ten for the operators to maintain a listening watch on its own wavelength for official instructions etc. Despite these incredible restrictions, Two-Emma-Toc became famous among the many amateurs now operating. Captain Peter Pendleton Eckersley directed the installation of the original transmitter in the Marconi Aircraft Development Section housed in a wooden hut at Writtle. P.P. Eckersley also proved to be a talented 'broadcaster' and received tremendous popularity from his Tuesday evening entertainments between 8.00 and 8.30 pm. Radio's first play (Cyrano de Bergerac) and a form of 'Children's Hour' (squeezed into the allotted time) were broadcast from Writtle during its short life time. It closed down on 17 January 1923 and the original hut still survives as a sports pavilion in the playing fields of a school in Chelmsford.

During 1922 there was a lot of activity in the world of broadcasting in Britain. A second Marconi station began transmissions from Marconi House in London with the call-sign 2LO. Metropolitan Vickers in Manchester (2ZY) and Western Electric in London (2WP — later to become 5IT Birmingham) also came into existence. The British

Broadcasting Company was formed on 18 October 1922; it was registered as a company on 15 December 1922 and received its Licence from the Post Office on 18 January 1923. The new broadcasting company consisted of the so-called 'Big Six' — Marconi's, Metro-Vickers, Western Electric, Radio Communication Co., General Electric and BTH (British Thomson-Houston) each of which had a representative on the board of directors. Two further independent directors (from Messrs. Siemens & Burndept) were also elected by the smaller firms. These small firms could become members of the BBC simply by purchasing a £1 share. All member companies of the BBC had to be *bona fide* British manufacturers.

The public were required to pay a 10 shilling licence fee when they acquired a wireless receiver and half of this went to finance the BBC. Initially, it was the intention to protect British industry from the strong foreign competition that could easily grow up as a result of the head start other countries (particularly the USA) had had in getting broadcasting under way. When a company wished to sell a receiver on the open market, the set had to be specially 'approved' by the Postmaster General. In the official words: 'Firms desiring to submit apparatus for approval and registration should send a sample of each type, together with relevant wiring diagrams, preferably of foolscap size, to the Engineer in Chief, Wireless Section, Room 8B, 4th Floor, General Post Office (North) London, EC1. Batteries, valves, and telephone receivers need not be sent with the apparatus for test. These accessories will be provided by the Post Office. After test, the firms will be notified of the result and advised that the sets are ready for collection.'

In order that a receiver be granted Post Office approval a few basic conditions had to be complied with. Among other things it was stated that, 'No receiving apparatus for general broadcast purposes shall contain a valve or valves so connected as to be capable of causing the aerial to oscillate.' It was also stated that only fixed reaction would be permitted on the first valve and adjustable reaction could be used on subsequent valves. The Post Office tests would include connecting the set to a 30ft and a 100ft aerial and checking its interference properties.

It is not clear from the records how stringently these conditions were applied. Most of the early valve sets that had good reception qualities could be mishandled and produce severe interference in neighbouring receivers. It is possible that 'oscillation' tests were abandoned by the Post Office at a very early stage. An editorial in the *Wireless World* of 23 January 1924, little more than a year after the commencement of the BBC, suggested that the only tests carried out when a set was undergoing 'approval' was in relation to wavelength range. This would certainly imply that the original intentions behind the GPO system of approval had become somewhat watered down or were simply too difficult in practice.

Receivers which had been granted the approval of the PMG then carried a special BBC stamp (Fig 36) around which were the words, 'Type approved by Post Master General.' The set also bore a registration number. Many hundreds of sets of every description were given registration numbers — ranging from the humblest crystal sets to very elaborate multi-valve sets. A close examination of the many sets that have survived reveals that the craftsmanship and manufacturing expertise was also wide ranging — from the very crudest badly designed sets to the most advanced designs housed in finely crafted cabinets. It is not known whether any of the sets submitted to the Post Office for approval *ever* failed the test!

Sets continued to carry the BBC stamp and a registration number until about the middle of 1924, after which registration was no longer necessary. Some manufacturers put the BBC stamp on components and accessories although it is not at all clear what the words, 'Type approved by the Post Master General' meant in such cases. The use of this and other indications of 'British Manufacture' were constantly debated between the BBC, government departments and manufacturers' organisations. But even though submission for approval and registration only applied to receivers, components and headphones and valves were frequently adorned with the BBC stamp. Certainly no registration numbers were issued for these items. Although registration was intended to apply primarily to receivers, amplifiers were also sometimes submitted and there are many examples bearing Post Office registration numbers. Perhaps, in the early 1920s, the distinction between a receiving set and a low frequency amplifier (or 'Note Magnifier' as it used to be called) was not as well drawn as it would be today. Some early so-called amplifiers during and after the First World War had a detector stage and could be used as receivers when a simple external tuning circuit was added.

Apart from the home-made receivers that abounded during the first two years of broadcasting, GPO registered sets constitute the full total of the sets that were available to the British public of the period. Of course, although foreign sets could not be officially imported at the time, some undoubtedly were and some manufacturers even managed to get registration numbers issued to imported sets . . . though very few.

It would be of significant historical interest to obtain an original list of manufacturers' GPO registration numbers and it would be a very great help to serious collectors of early 1920's receivers. As far as can be determined at the time of publishing this book, no such list has survived. It may seem incredible that such an important document could have been destroyed for whatever reason. From today's point of view, it may well seem unlikely that such a list could contain information sufficient to warrant its destruction, but there were many sensitive questions arising at the time and some manufacturers thought the whole thing a farce. After all, an ordinary individual could make his own set to any old specifications he liked at a cost of 10/- for an experimenter's licence (or 15/- for a constructors licence between October 1923 and July 1924) — and *he* didn't have to send *his* set to the Post office for approval.

So, by mid 1924, the PMG did not require approval of type from manufacturers and by the beginning of 1925, British manufacturers would have to face foreign competition. Many British manufacturers continued to use the BBC stamp in a modified form as shown in Fig 37. This was, at first glance, the same as the existing stamp but, around the perimeter were the words: 'Entirely British Manufacture'. Perhaps the buying public had come to expect this BBC stamp as a sort of 'good quality' sign and were more inclined to buy sets with the new stamp than sets with no stamp at all.

The incredible variety of receivers that were available to the British public only a few years after the BBC came into existence can be seen from a brief glance at contemporary advertising. Many hundreds of companies were involved in some form of wireless equipment or component manufacture during the first five years of broadcasting. By the end of 1925 there were 1716 member companies of the BBC and only 77 of these were non-manufacturing dealers. Some of the very small 'one-man' companies were making very crude crystal or valve receivers and selling them at low prices to attract the large fraction of the population who simply could not afford to buy the more expensive sets being made by the larger companies. In the 1926/27 catalogues, the cheapest two valve set available was one made by the Brownie Wireless Co. for £4.16.0. including valves and royalties (see Fig 79). A working man in the early 1920s could well have been earning less than £2 per week and throughout the 20s there were over a million unemployed. To such people, wireless sets at a cost of over £40 or even the 'very popular' Marconiphone two valve set (Fig 38) at a cost of £19.4.6. (including valves, batteries, headphones and royalties) must have seemed a bit out of reach. Of course it must be remembered that at this time, a large portion of the population accepted a situation in which what have become quite ordinary domestic appliances were considered 'luxury goods' and very much out of their reach. It is always difficult when looking back in time, into a completely different social context than the present, to make reliable assessments of the accessibility of goods in terms of wages and prices. Average wage and indeed cost-of-living index can be quite deceptive. During the 1920s and 30s, in spite of heavy unemployment, there was a rise in average living standards and the price of a wireless set at the time was probably not very surprising to anybody from whatever wage category.

However, a wireless set was a new 'toy' and, in all its varied forms, it began to creep into all levels of society. The first person in the street to get a set would become the centre of attraction in those well-knit communities where social gatherings could take place at any time in anybody's house. Crystal sets were made by fathers and sons to murmers of admiration from wives, mums and sisters. BBC licences were bought by the thousand each month — there were well over two million by the end of 1926 when the British Broadcasting Company became a corporation. Most wireless sets were listened to regularly by the whole family and, when this is combined with the large number of 'licence evaders' known to exist, it is probable that there were about twelve million regular listeners to the daily broadcasts from the BBC. During these early years, the wireless set slowly evolved from the laboratory apparatus and government surplus stock used by experimenters before 1922. The evolution was cautious. Manufacturers produced mahogany, walnut and oak boxes with drawers, lids and doors, in which the apparatus could be hidden. The 1920s was a period of groping, a thrusting out in all directions, and both the technical aspects of circuit design and the appearance of the set itself remained very fluid until the early 1930s.

Domestic wireless receivers of the 1920s can be divided into three distinct categories:

I. *1922—1924* During this period manufacturers had to have their sets approved by the GPO and they will all bear the BBC stamp and a registration number. Figs 39—60 illustrate typical examples of the crystal sets and Figs 61—66 show a few of the valve receivers from this early period. Many of these clearly show how the cabinet work was merely a box to contain an 'unsightly instrument'. There were many home-made sets during the period (Figs 67 & 68) and these did not have to be 'type approved' by the GPO much to the annoyance of some manufacturers.

II. *1925—1927* At first the appearance of wireless sets did not change much and many of them were made with components from the first period by small manufacturers. Figs 69—77 show some of the crystal sets which didn't appear in time to get a GPO number. Some of the manufacturers continued to use the modified BBC stamp (Figs 37 & 70) surrounded by the words 'Entirely British Manufacture'. There was no obligation to use such a stamp but doubtless it had some prestige value. Also, as important restrictions had been lifted in 1925, manufacturers probably felt that some customers would like a means of distinguishing between 'British made' and 'Foreign' items. Figs 78—87 show a few of the valve sets of this second period.

III. *1927—1929* During this last period, the British Broadcasting Company had been replaced by the new Corporation with J.C.W. Reith as its first Director General. Domestic wireless sets began to acquire a more distinctive appearance quite unlike the standard boxes and cabinets that had previously been used to hide the works. Technical developments were making the 'All Mains' sets more available (Figs 88 & 89) allowing designers to concentrate on a tidy container uncluttered by unsightly battery leads or rows of battery terminals. The horn loudspeaker was also slowly disappearing to be replaced by the balanced armature speaker with a lightweight paper cone or by the moving coil speaker. Designers had, on occasions, attempted to put the old horn speaker into a wireless cabinet and some very ingenious horns had been designed to achieve this. However, the balanced armature and the moving coil speakers were much better suited to the purpose and, during the latter part of the 1920s, completely self-contained wireless sets began to develop. Metal and bakelite cabinets made their appearance (Figs 90 & 91) but wood remained the dominant material for cabinet making.

LOUDSPEAKERS

The horn loudspeaker, as we have seen, began to disappear from the scene towards the latter part of the 1920s. Other types of loudspeaker had been available for some time. The embrionic forms of cone speaker can be traced back to 1879 and the principle of the moving coil speaker was described in a patent specification (Number 9712) by Sir Oliver Lodge in 1898. Several very elegant cone speakers were available from even before 1922 and the moving coil cone loudspeaker of C.L. Farrand was described in 1921. The pleated diaphragm Sterling 'Primax' (Fig 92) manufactured in this country under 'Lumière' patents, was fitted into large cabinet sets made by the Sterling Company early in the 1920s.

The horn speaker reigned supreme throughout the 1920s and continued to stand proudly on top of or beside the wireless box. For the listening public, there was a vast number of horn speakers to choose from and Figs 93—98 show only a very small selection. One manufacturer, the BTH Company, brought out a simplified speaker (the so-called C2) with a moulded bakelite base which enabled them to sell it at the very competitive price of £3. Over a million of them were made and many survive for collectors today (Fig 98). The same company began manufacturing the Rice-Kellogg moving coil loudspeaker in 1925 only a year after they had introduced the earlier version of their C2 horn.

Of course, the horn speaker had far too functional an appearance for many people and, just as they had furniture-like boxes to hide the wireless apparatus in, so many attempts were made to introduce speakers that did not look like speakers. Horns were 'folded' into mahogany boxes (Fig 99) or were hidden in glazed pottery figures (Figs 100—101) and even a papier mâché Confucius (Fig 102). But for those listeners who did not mind the horn appearance, and perhaps even relished its functionality, horns came in all shapes and sizes. Fig 103 shows a tall elegant horn on the left with a miniature one on the right and one of the 'folded' encased varieties in between. The reflex horn could be made very lightweight (Fig 104) and of similar dimensions to the paper cone speaker. The lightweight cone speakers allowed more elegant shapes to appear (Figs 105 & 106) and were used extensively in portable sets.

AMERICAN SETS

Apart from the vast number of British sets that were available to the buying public, large numbers of imported sets were making their appearance in the shops towards the end of the 1920s. The manufacturing industry in the USA was understandably very active and there is little doubt that a technically better product was available to the American public. In this country multi-valve sets were simply too expensive for most people and manufacturers concentrated their efforts on the simpler sets which sold well. Crystal sets also continued to sell here throughout the 1920s as this was all that many people could possibly afford. In the USA multi-valve sets were quite commonplace from early in the 1920s and both 'Neutrodyne' and 'Superheterodyne' sets were made in vast numbers.

The Neutrodyne set (Patented by Prof Hazeltine in the USA and by John Scott-Taggart in Britain) relied on special circuitry in the anode circuit of the high frequency amplifying valves to neutralise the capacitance effects of the internal valve electrodes. Such an arrangement allowed the use of several H.F. valve stages without the dreadful instability which would otherwise result. Several manufacturers made these sets in this country but only in very small numbers and, in general, they only sold to skilled operators or serious amateurs. In contrast, they sold very widely in the USA much to the delight of Prof. Hazeltine who took the precaution of buying John Scott-Taggart's patents.

The Superheterodyne sets available in this country were also either imported from the USA or, like the Burndept illustrated in Fig 107, produced by 'quality' British companies prepared to indulge in small scale production of luxury sets.

The principle of the supersonic heterodyne set, or 'superhet' as it became familiarly known, is to change the frequency of the incoming signal to a lower fixed frequency by means of 'beating' it with a locally produced oscillator signal. This lower fixed frequency, called an intermediate frequency, is then amplified by circuits that are very insensitive to all other frequencies. This arrangement eventually became the universal approach to receiver design and remains so today. The principal name associated with the invention of the superhet is Major E.H. Armstrong. He invented this method of reception while serving with the American Expeditionary Force during the First World War. His patent application, however, was some six months behind that of W. Schottky in Germany who first presented the idea in his company's (Siemens) house journal (25 February to 6 March 1918) and filed a patent application on 18 June 1918. However, Schottky's proposals remained undeveloped. During 1918, Major Armstrong had been experimenting with an eight valve superhet constructed by the Signal Corps and was thus the first man to investigate the practical capabilities of this type of receiver. His patent application is dated 30 December 1918.

Although the superheterodyne principle came into being in 1918, the idea of using a locally generated signal and 'beating' this with the incoming signal was not at all new. One of the most remarkable and imaginative experimenters in the history of radio, Reginald A. Fessenden (see also page 37), filed a patent covering the idea on September 28 1901. At first he did not use a local oscillator but rather had the transmitter send out both of the frequencies from which he was to derive a beat frequency. When he later used a local oscillator, he called it a 'heterodyne' which derives from Greek; Heteros (other or external) and Dynamis (force). The heterodyne method eventually gave rise to the superheterodyne principle in which the beat frequency was well above the audible range.

60

Although American receivers of the 1920s included more complex designs than were normally available in this country, the appearance of their sets also show the primitive tendency to hide an instrument in a box. The distinctive wireless set with its loudspeaker grill, tuning dial and control knobs made its appearance at about the same time as it did in this country at the end of the 1920s. The full golden age of development of these classic receivers did not occur until the early 1930s. Some American receivers of the 1920s are illustrated in Figures 108-124.

SOME TECHNICAL DEVELOPMENTS OF THE 1920s

Before leaving the 1920s, mention should be made of a few of the technical features which grew up during the period. As has already been mentioned, the neutrodyne and the superhet were available in some form throughout the 20s but gained little popularity in this country. Most receivers were of the simplest possible design. All had a simple tuning circuit to select the required station and most sets relied on some form of 'positive feed back' in which some of the signal coming out of an amplifying valve was fed back into an earlier stage. This arrangement helped enormously in the amplifying process and it also helped to improve selectivity. A typical simple reaction circuit is shown in Figure 32. One unfortunate feature of this type of reaction circuit is that the power being fed back could, if slightly overdone, produce violent oscillations which could then be re-radiated by the aerial. In this way disturbances could be set up in other radio sets in the district and, as most people had high outside aerials, the disturbance could be quite considerable. During the early days of broadcasting, certain types of reaction circuits were illegal but this did not prevent the howling wails of badly tuned neighbouring receivers from being a very common experience. Broadcast announcements were made appealing to listeners to control their sets carefully and to adjust their reaction knobs with due regard to other users.

To distinguish these sets with a tuned hf stage from the later superhets, they are frequently called TRF receivers — meaning 'tuned radio frequency'. The TRF set was in use well into the 1930s and, when well designed, was very competitive with the superhet.

When we examine the very simple volume control circuits that have been in use since the 1930s, we can't help wondering why it was not introduced much earlier than it was. In the 1920s, many sets did not have any volume control at all. Most sets however relied on the filament current rheostat or on the reaction control for making adjustments to volume. The filament control approach was fraught with problems because using it to reduce the volume inevitably increased the distortion. The reaction control was a much better approach and the reaction control knob was often marked 'volume' with an arrow indicating the direction of increase. But again distortion was never very far away and correct adjustment of a set remained one of those skills (like winding the grandfather clock) that was reserved for the master of the house or the precocious son.

Prior to 1927 the radio valve was a simple triode. There were three electrodes: an anode, a grid and a filament, just as Lee de Forest had originally designed his audion in 1907. The triode valve came in all shapes and sizes (Figs.125-130). Special valves were made for high frequency amplification, others for detection and others for low frequency amplification. Selecting an appropriate valve for a particular set was often a matter of trying out one after the other. They all worked to some extent and one simply selected the valve which functioned best. Some valves were available with a second grid called bi-grid valves. The purpose of these valves was a bit uncertain and some circuits were designed which attempted to eliminate the use of the high voltage battery which was a very expensive outlay once every six months or so for owners of all normal receivers. So bi-grid valves were claimed occasionally to be great 'battery savers' etc. However, although a circuit could be designed successfully without the use of a high voltage battery, no satisfactory loudspeaking receiver was ever developed and the bi-grid valve remained only a source of curiosity to enthusiastic 'experimenters'.

In 1927 however, a new valve made its appearance. This was the so-called screened grid valve and it, like its bi-grid precursor, had two grids and hence four electrodes and eventually acquired the name 'tetrode'. The idea of the screened grid was to reduce the capacitative coupling between grid and anode which resulted in so much instability in the normal triode when used as an HF amplifier. Thus the screened grid valve allowed designers to introduce a good highly stable high gain HF stage at the front end of the otherwise fairly conventional circuit. The screened grid valve (the S625) which first appeared (Fig.131) in this country was designed by H.J. Round of the Marconi Company in 1926 and introduced early in 1927. It remained in the horizontally mounted form for only about one year and then became a normal four pin upright valve (the S215) with the connection to the control grid on top of the valve. The screened grid valve appeared at about the same time in the USA and their first commercially successful screened grid valve was the

UX222 which had been under development for some time at General Electric and appeared on the market late in 1927.

The screened grid valve was the first departure from the ubiquitous triode and it was soon joined by valves with three grids (pentodes) for power amplification. The 1930s saw a large number of multi-electrode valves including valves which were really two or more valves in one envelope. The idea of mounting several valves in one envelope began in the 1926-27 period and one of the best examples of the multivalve was developed by the Loewe company in Germany. This valve, which first appeared at the Berlin Wireless Exhibition in September 1926, consisted of three triodes and also all the interconnecting components. The concept was quite a long way ahead of its time and might now be looked upon as one of the first examples of an integrated circuit. Only a couple of external tuning components was required to make this Loewe valve (the 3NF) into a complete three valve receiver (Fig.132). The three filaments in the 3NF were quite vulnerable because, if one of them failed, the whole valve was useless. However, the manufacturers offered the very special service of replacing all three filaments if one of them failed at a cost of 8 shillings (40p). The original valve cost 25 shillings and 3 pence (£1.26) and considering that this was virtually a three valve set it was quite cheap even by the standards of the time. The set illustrated is still functioning and performs extremely well. The idea was novel but not lasting. It was an extreme example of virtuosity in the new valve industry but hardly affected the trends that were establishing themselves in the saner branches of the industry. A three valve multi-valve was also available on the American market about a year later, developed and marketed in some joint manner by the Emerson company and the Cleartron Vacuum Tube Company. This valve however did not have the interconnecting components inside the envelope. In this respect the Loewe valve is unique and the place it has in history is far more than that of a simple curiosity.

One final development worthy of note from the 1920s is, of course, the all-mains receiver. Throughout the 1920s there was a constant demand for a wireless set that could be operated directly from the alternating current supply and there were various attempts at achieving this. The high voltage battery could be quite easily eliminated using a transformer, a rectifier valve and one or two other components. An example of a Marconi high tension battery eliminator is shown in Fig.133. Replacing the low tension battery with a transformer and other components was not so easy, as the filament of the valve which required the low tension battery would easily transmit the alternating current frequency as an

63

undesirable 'hum' in the loudspeaker. This could be reduced but it was difficult to eliminate altogether. There was obviously a need for a valve which could be directly supplied with an alternating current.

The indirectly heated cathode became the solution to this problem. In this sort of valve the surface which emits the electrons does not carry the heating current. It is a specially treated surface which, when heated by a nearby filament, emits a copious supply of electrons. Such a device had been constructed by A.M. Nicolson of Western Electric as early as 1914. But successful commercial valves using this principle did not appear in this country until 1926. The Marconi-Osram Valve Company produced their KL1 in late 1926 and it was fully described in *Wireless World* in January 1927. Also in 1926, E.Y. Robinson of Metropolitan Vickers developed a 'slip-coated' heater technique for the efficient construction of a valve with an indirectly heated cathode which enabled this company to produce what turned out to be the world's prototype for all subsequent indirectly heated valves in late 1927. This was designated the Metrovick-AC/R. In the USA the first examples of the alternating current indirectly heated cathode valves appeared at about the same time. The Radiotron UX225 appeared in the spring of 1927 and the UY227 came out a few weeks later. Of all those early AC valves, that designed by E.Y. Robinson and manufactured by Metrovick as the AC/R takes a special place in history. It was not the first indirectly heated cathode valve to be made but it was the first of the type that was to be the standard product of the giant valve industry for the next 35 years until the valve was finally replaced by the transistor.

A BRIEF LOOK AT THE 1930s

The wireless set evolved from childhood to early youth in the 1920s. It grew to full maturity during the 1930s. Early in the 1930s the TRF receivers and Superhets were still jostling for supremacy but by the middle of the decade, the Superhet had become commonplace. Technology had advanced considerably over those early attempts at the start of the broadcasting era and was now able to provide at quite moderate cost a set that was highly selective, very reliable and usually mains operated. The battery operated set still persisted throughout the 1930s and even the 1940s because there were many homes which still had no electricity supply both in town and country. Even in the 1940s it was a familiar sight to see people taking their lead-acid accumulators to the radio or cycle shop for re-charging. It was very expensive to run a battery receiver particularly as by this time, listeners were using their sets for several hours each day.

The appearance of the wireless set in the 1930s was profoundly influenced by the growing use of moulded plastics. Bakelite had been in use from the 1920s. Fig.91 shows a small Pye receiver from about 1929 which was constructed of moulded bakelite and already one can see the rounded corners that are so easily produced by this technique. But as the 1930s moved on, so the technology of bakelite moulding became influenced by designers of reputation.

The Ekco AD65 (Fig.153) is a well known example of the work of Wells Coates and first appeared in 1934. This round shape marks a distinct break with traditional furniture design and it occurred at a time when the new materials were to be found struggling against the old for admission into the domestic environment. Black bakelite and chrome were trying to edge out mahogany and walnut in the avant garde circles of furniture design. The radio set itself had by the mid 1930s become the very centre of the home. As had always been the case, families would sit around the fire-side in the evening, but the conversation of earlier generations was slowly giving way to the news and entertainment that poured ceaselessly from the newcomer, the radio. Frequently, the radio set would be placed on a high table as if on a pedestal. It was no longer an instrument hidden inside a box. It was now a functional furniture unit and had to be given as much design consideration as any other item of furniture.

Other designers were involved in creating the radio shapes of the 1930s. R.D. Russel and A.F. Thwaites designed sets for the Murphy Company, Wells Coates and Serge Chermayeff produced the Ekco designs of the period. A few well known British receivers from the 1930s are shown in Figs.153-160.

In the United States, a classical furniture style lingered in the design of radio sets. The Gothic arch or Cathedral shape, as it was called, was very common throughout the 1930s and such sets are becoming highly collectable there today. While the drawing rooms of America were accepting larger and larger radios, some having beautiful veneers and mouldings, there was also a trend at miniaturisation. Very small very compact sets were made for use in bedrooms, kitchens and recreation rooms. Figs.161-167 show a few of the typical domestic receivers in use in the USA during the 1930s.

With the onset of wartime restrictions at the end of the 1930s, the radio set acquired an even greater importance in the home than ever before. Now families would come together around their sets to listen to the good and bad news every day. Wireless sets or extension speakers were taken into the air-raid shelter. Wireless programmes were relayed over speaker systems in factories. Highly sophisticated communications receivers were used on ships, and aeroplanes and by the infantry. Long distance communication was a commonplace thing and altogether the world was a different place than it had been a mere forty or so years before, when Marconi had filed the world's first radio patent.

To the enthusiastic collector of radio relics it is impossible to give a complete account of the story. When a new collector starts to acquire equipment, he is often unaware of the vast number of manufacturers that came into existence during the 1920s. Many hundreds of manufacturers were involved in the new industry, some lasting for only a few months before being swept out of business by their more successful competitors. Only the larger companies survived and many of the smaller ones vanished without trace. Some were absorbed and brand names were often kept going by new owners.

Historians of the subject now find it extremely difficult to acquire all the information necessary to reconstruct complete histories of radio companies. As time goes by, the need to record this history will increase but the wherewithall will diminish. To give the collector some idea of the extent of the radio industry, an analysis of one single year is presented (see appendix). The year chosen is 1926 and, simply from those manufacturers who were prepared to advertise or have their names included in contemporary 'buyer's guides' such as the one published by *Wireless World* it can be deduced that there were well over 70 firms making and selling wireless sets in 1926. The customer who went out to get a set could choose any one of about 97 different crystal sets, 25 valve-crystal receivers, 38 1-valve sets, 127 2-valve sets, 128 3-valve sets and 163 sets with 4 or more valves. He could also choose from 41 different portable sets. The vast majority of these sets were of British origin and imported sets supplied by many dealers could also be added to this formidable list. It is interesting to note that, although small cheap sets were in great demand, there were more sets available with four or more valves than any other category.

Apart from the manufacturers of complete radio sets, there were a large number of manufacturers making radio components of all sorts. Firms ranging from one-man 'cottage industries' to huge enterprises were supplying the radio industry with loudspeakers, headphones, valves, transformers, wireless cabinets, engraved panels, tuning dials, terminals, plugs and sockets, batteries, battery eliminators and a host of other supporting devices.

The modern collector and historian of wireless soon finds it necessary to specialise if he is not to be swamped by the almost unending list of trade marks and manufacturers' names.

CURIOSITIES, ADVERTISING AND OTHER EPHEMERA

Apart from the serious business of manufacturing wireless sets in the 1920s, the radio topic crept into all walks of life. The occasional manufacturer went to great lengths to produce something quite out of the ordinary. Fig.134 shows a quite extraordinary set designed by Horace William Adey in 1929. This 4-valve receiver had many design features that made it perhaps the most truly portable set of its day. It performed better than many much larger sets and was just one of the many successful but highly individualistic sets made by Adey Radio Ltd. In 1930 this company produced a small 'cigar box' regenerative receiver for use by Scotland Yard and, would you believe it, fitted the loudspeaker drive unit into the policeman's helmet!

Many companies produced crystal sets that were 'different' and two of the most well known of these are shown in Figs.135-137. The idea of making crystal sets in an unusual form persisted into the 1930s and 1940s. Figs.138 and 139 show some of these later sets, many of which appeared in the form of current model radio sets.

Fig.140 shows a couple of disguised radio aerials, one in the form of a painted lion and the other in the form of a picture frame which became totally unrecognisable when fitted with a suitable family photograph.

Apart from the great variety of loudspeakers already referred to, the occasional 'special' also appeared. Fig.141 shows a tortoise shell speaker highly rated by the manufacturers and probably quite a practical device to have by the bed-side.

Visitors to the seaside on the look out for bits of souvenir china could find many examples of the wireless motif in the shops (Fig.142). Smokers had their 'wireless' tobacco and could collect series of cigarette cards dealing with the subject (Fig.143).

During the 1920s there were many wireless magazines ranging from the very popular to the highly technical. Fig.144 shows one of the very popular magazines which catered to the needs of the home constructor. *Wireless World* (Fig.145) advertised that 'by general consent', theirs was the 'best all-round wireless magazine in the world'. The magazines were of course full of advertising and, as can be seen from Figs.146-148, intimate family scenes were often invoked to create the right atmosphere.

Cartoons of every description appeared in the 1920s and the subject of wireless frequently occurred. Seaside post cards used the theme from the early 20s (Fig.149) until the war years (Fig.150). Two delightful cartoon paintings apeared in the early days of broadcasting. These were done by Albert Kaye and were bought in oak frames with engraved ivorine captions. Fig.151 shows the 'little husband' who finally learned how to entertain his talkative wife. Fig.152 shows how happiness could be provided by the BBC to the lonely spinster who, for the first time in her life, had a man say good night to her ... while in bed!'

THE ROLE OF THE COLLECTOR

There is a great temptation among new collectors to spend a lot of time and effort 'renovating' old wireless sets as they come into their possession. Unfortunately a lot of so-called renovation can only be described as 'destruction'. Whatever the place of the early wireless set may be at present, it will certainly become of great antique value in the future. Those sets which have been lovingly stripped and re-varnished will be comparatively valueless in the future when seen alongside the more fortunate, though perhaps dirtier, examples that have escaped the vandalism of the amateur bodger. The serious collector already avoids anything but the untouched originals.

Renovation occasionally demands replacement of components or parts of components and high quality 'replicas' can be made. However, a replica is generally recognised as such by the expert eye of a veteran collector. If replicas are manufactured in quantity and are 'indistinguishable' from originals then, without any doubt, they are fakes. If such manufactured articles *are* distinguishable from the originals because they are 'not quite right' then they are worthless rubbish. How do we escape from this dilemma? There is occasionally an obvious need for providing a well made 'replica' to complete the task of refurbishing an old relic. If exact replicas can be made, they should be stamped or engraved with some indication that they are not originals. I personally think that a simple date stamp indicating the year of manufacture is sufficient and necessary. If a society, or other organisation such as a museum, sponsors the reproduction of replica components, valves, panels, knobs, cabinets etc then, as well as a date stamp the insignia of the organisation should be included.

There have already been many good quality replica components made by and for enthusiastic collectors. Some of them have been marketed as 'the real thing' and are therefore blatant fakes. Others have been more quietly introduced but are still to be treated as fakes and will contribute

68

to a certain bewilderment and confusion among future historians, museum keepers and collectors. Every effort should be made by the serious collector to avoid the temptation to add to this confusion.

The role of the collector of old wireless sets is an extremely important one. At the time of writing this book, private collectors in Britain own between them a far greater wealth of equipment than can as yet be found in the museums. Of course it is true that the unique items handled by the great pioneers are for the most part to be found in such places as the Science Museum, London. But apart from this, private ownership constitutes the finest existing museum of wireless history, albeit a 'collective one'. As in any museum, the equipment in private hands should be well documented. A British Vintage Wireless Society was formed in 1976 and is slowly developing a register of the contents of this very extensive 'collective museum'. As the generations pass, this distributed collection will frequently change hands and slowly sort itself out until a time will come when the very best pieces will be gathered together in museums where they can be professionally looked after. It is therefore incumbent upon the present owners to concentrate their efforts on 'preservation' and, apart from some occasional expert attention, should practice a lot of restraint in their renovation efforts. This may seem an unnecessarily hard line to take in view of all the beautiful examples of highly polished restored sets that can be seen in private collections. But this superficial beauty, this cosmetic face-lifting, is no part of serious collecting and constitutes the biggest danger of private ownership. As long as we treat collecting as an amateur pursuit or hobby then of course the owners must be allowed to get their enjoyment in any way they wish. Collectors however, quickly aspire to a high degree of professionalism and the very best collectors are probably caring for their equipment and learning to understand it with a higher level of competence than can be found in most museums. Some of the worst examples of cosmetic restoration can be seen in museums.

Collecting and looking after old radio sets and studying the history of the subject is quite a fascinating occupation and is one which can only be done by the vast army of private collectors ferreting out hardware and ephemeral remnants of past decades. It is hoped that this book will provide a perspective and a guide to the subject particularly for those second generation collectors who were born after the transistor revolution and to whom valve technology is a new discovery. Most of the present day collectors were brought up in the 'valve age' and are steeped in valve lore. As the years pass, so will the old brigade, and newcomers will have the daunting task of coming to grips with an advanced technology that has long since been superseded by other more relevant technologies.

As we leave this brief look at the coming of the wireless age it is interesting to note that the transistor itself has already acquired something of the 'patina' of antiquity and is nudging its way into wireless history as the age of the integrated 'chip' pushes aside the discrete components of the past. And so the transistor comes to join its solid state ancestors, the crystal detector and perhaps some of the primitive detectors of David Hughes of one hundred years ago.

Fig 36 The Post Master General's stamp of approval which appeared, together with an official GPO registration number, on all receivers on sale to the public between autumn 1922 and mid 1924. It was also used without any official status and without a registration number on some valves, headphones and other components.

Fig 37 This unofficial stamp was used by some manufacturers from about the beginning of 1925 until 1927.

Fig 38 The Marconiphone V2. This set came in two versions, the V2 and the V2A but there was no circuit difference between them. The very early version of the V2 however had no regenerative circuitry and lacked the plug-in regenerator unit on the right hand side ... these early versions are very rare. GPO Numbers: V2, 2001; V2A, 0175.

Fig 39 Belling Lee crystal set. GPO Number 4553

Fig 40 Two crystal sets by Burndept, the 'Junior' (GPO No.113) and the Ethophone No.1, Mk III (This set appeared after the GPO No. period)

Fig 41 The Cosmos crystal receiver in moulded case 'Type Approved' but GPO number not known.

Fig 42 (above) Edison Bell crystal set.
Oak box. Two crystals. Manufactured
in this country by J.E. Hough Ltd.,
Edison Bell Works, London, SE15.
GPO No.615

Fig 43 (above right) Ediswan Model
1924 crystal set. Slide tuning. GPO
No.4385

Fig 44 (below right) Ericsson Crystal
set, type 0/1002. Oak box GPO
No.280

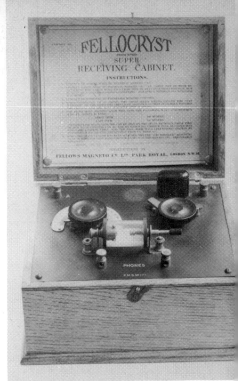

Fig 45 Ericsson Crystal set, type 0/1050. Miniature, turned polished ebonite. Cardboard container is 2″ square and 1½″ deep. GPO No.5228

Fig 46 Fellowcryst GPO No.177. Oak box.

Fig 47 Exactly same as Fig.46 but this version has multi-hole terminals for connecting several sets of headphones.

74

Fig 48 (above) Gecophone No.1.
Mahogany box. This set also came in a
version with a glass enclosed crystal.
GPO No.102

Fig 49 (above right) Gecophone No.2.
Mahogany box. This set incorporates a
buzzer which enabled the crystal to be
correctly adjusted when there was no
signal available at the aerial terminal.
GPO No.103

Fig 50 (below right) H.E.W., London.
GPO No.639

75

Fig 51 The Maxitone crystal set. GPO No. illegible but probably 4 figures indicating that it first appeared on the market in the spring of 1924.

Fig 52 The OTB crystal set. GPO No.745. Turned wood.

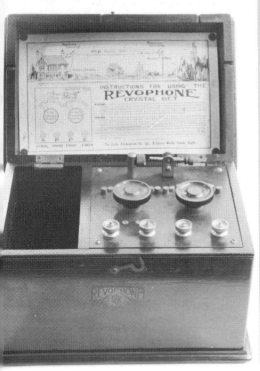

Fig 53 The Revophone crystal set. Mahogany box. GPO No.669. Made by Cable Accessories Co.

Fig 54 The Rexophone with double crystal. GPO No.792. Made by Morch Bros. Ltd.

Fig 55 The R.I. crystal set type XLA No.727. Made by Radio Industries Ltd. GPO No.122.

77

Fig 56 The Sparta crystal set. Made about the 1923/24 period but the GPO registration number is not known.

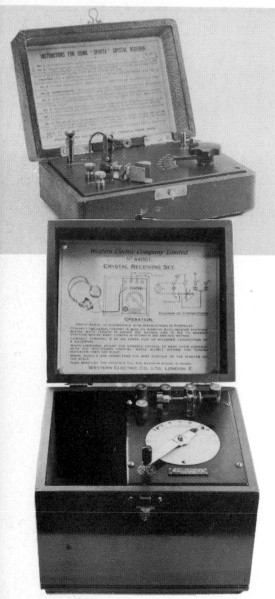

Fig 57 The T.M.C. crystal set made by the Telephone Manufacturing Co. GPO No.183.

Fig 58 The Western Electric Crystal set. Fine mahogany box. Identical sets were manufactured in the USA and Britain simultaneously. GPO No.134.

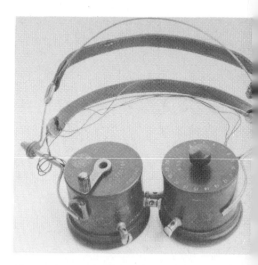

Fig 59 A crystal set built into a pair of headphones. Manufacturer unknown. GPO No.4145.

Fig 60 An example of a 'foreign' set that could not be imported. Made by H. Jacobi of Vienna probably in the 1922-24 period. After use the crystal platform can be inverted. A spare plug-in crystal is shown on the left. The mains plug was provided to utilise one's house wiring as an aerial.

Fig 61 Gecophone two valve set (Detector and LF transformer coupled). The set is sitting on top of a two-valve amplifier. On the left is a telephone distribution board to enable up to six people to listen. The amplifier was normally intended to go with a Gecophone set of similar appearance but having an H.F. and detector with reactance coupling. Type BC3200.

Fig 62 Gecophone two valve flat-top set. Detector, LF. Type BC3250

Fig 63 Marconiphone valve crystal receiver. This set utilises a V24 valve and a carborundum detector in a reflex circuit similar to the Marconiphone V2. Surprisingly the GPO No. of this set is not known. It was printed on the leatherette and all existing sets examined have had the number scuffed off! Type RB10

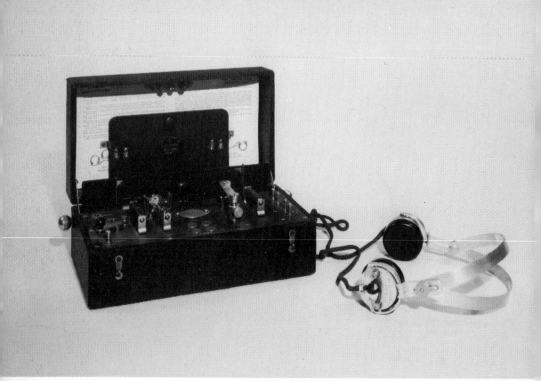

Fig 64 BTH (British Thomson-Houston Co. Ltd., Rugby) H.F. valve, crystal detector receiver. GPO No.0373

Fig 65 Fellowphone Super Two manufactured by the Fellows Magneto Co., Ltd.) H.F. and detector. GPO No.226. The speaker is by TMC.

Fig 66 (below) The Ashley 3 valve set (2 HF Detector) made by Ashley Wireless Telephone Co., Liverpool. The plug-in coils for various wavelength ranges can be seen in racks. GPO No.0155

Fig 67 (below right) A home-made set of about 1924. Detector 2LF transformer coupled.

81

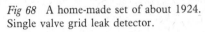
Fig 68 A home-made set of about 1924. Single valve grid leak detector.

Fig 70 Tubular crystal set made by J.W.B. Wireless Company. This company was later called Brownie Wireless Co. and the sets were called 'Brownie'. Note the later version of the BBC stamp. Earlier versions of this model bore the GPO No.4155.

Fig 69 Arbon Daventry crystal set made by R.R. & Co. of Birmingham.

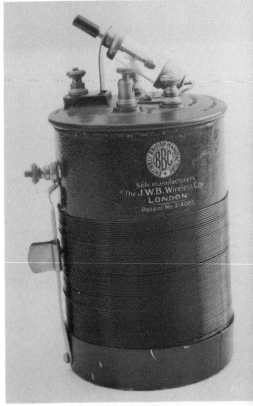

82

Fig 71 Brownie No.2 crystal set made by Brownie Wireless Co. This is seen linked to a microphone amplifier and H2 speaker both made by S.G. Brown Ltd.

Fig 72 BCM/JR (believed to be by Jean Rigaut, London). Supplied by H.G. Richardson, Boscombe.

Fig 74 Believed to be made by Ward &
Goldstone Ltd., Frederick Rd.,
Pendleton, Manchester. An example of a
sliding inductance tuner.

Fig 76 The '447' tapped inductance
tuning with loading coil.

Fig 73 The Efescaphone made by Falk
Stadelmann & Co. Ltd. The 'Benbow'
model.

Fig 75 The Fortevox Junior crystal set
made by F. & G. Hornsey, London, N.8.

Fig 77 Gecophone 'Junior'.

Fig 78 The AJS made by A.J. Stevens & Co. Ltd., Wolverhampton. A quality receiver of the 1924/5 period.

Fig 79 Brownie 2-valve set. Made by Brownie Wireless Co. who specialised in moulded cases.

Fig 80 Burndept's Duplex VA in black composition moulded case.

Fig 81 Chakophone No.1B three valve set. Detector and 2 L.F. transformer coupled in Jacobean oak cabinet. 1925/6 Made by the Eagle Engineering Co. Ltd., Eagle Works, Warwick.

Fig 82 The Chakophone 'Junior Two' also made by Eagle Engineering Co. Ltd.

Fig 83 The Cosmos 'Cruet' set made by Metropolitan Vickers Electrical Co. Ltd., Trafford Park, Manchester. Black moulded composition material. 1924/5.

Fig 84 The Edison Bell 'Bijou' two valve set of about 1926.

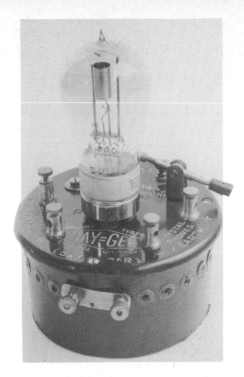

Fig 85 The Gecophone 2 valve set (BC 2720). Detector, L.F. with variable aerial reactance unit. Transformer coupled.

Fig 86 Jay-Gee crystal-one valve set.

Fig 87 Pye 222 two valve set. Detector and L.F. with plug-in coils at rear. This set is shown connected to the Sterling 'Dinkie' loudspeaker. The set has a black metal panel and sides and an oak box. The speaker is light brown.

Fig 88 Gambrell Model C2DC mains operated set. Made in about 1927. This was one of the first British mains sets commercially available.

Fig 89 Philips mains operated receiver Model 2514 made in 1928.

Fig 90 Gecophone Model BC2930 Victor 3. This small 3 valve battery receiver has wooden base and top and a crackle finish metal case.

Fig 91 Pye 232 in moulded bakelite case. The use of bakelite was cautious at this stage but soon began to have an impact on cabinet design. This is a 2 valve battery operated set. c 1928

Fig 92 The Sterling Primax pleated diaphragm speaker. 1923/4

Fig 93 Western Electric speaker. 21ins high. Ebonite horn.

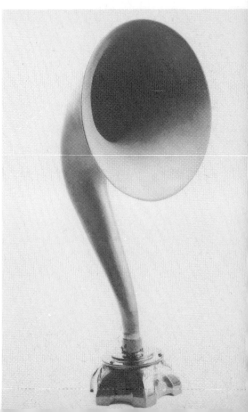

Fig 94 Small speaker by S.G. Brown. 10½ins high.

Fig 95 The Crystavox speaker by S.G. Brown. This speaker has a built-in microphone amplifier — a speciality of this company. The knob on the amplifier cover has a magnet attached to it which finely controls the balance of the amplifier armature.

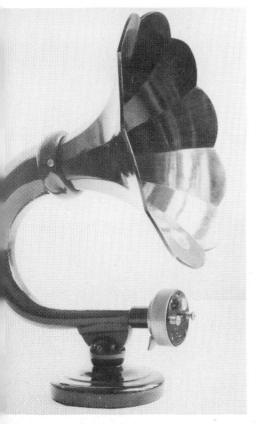

Fig 96 Speaker made by 'Walbro — All Wood Products'. A Brown type U drive unit is attached to this speaker which is made entirely of wood.

91

Fig 97 B.T.H. 'Loud Speaking Telephone' Type D form C1 made about 1922.

Fig 98 B.T.H. C2 speaker first introduced in 1924. It gradually evolved into this streamlined bakelite and aluminium version and was still available in the late 1920s. Over a million of them were made.

Fig 99 Boxed folded horn speaker by
S.G. Brown. 8½ins high × 11¼ins ×
13¾ins.

Fig 100 A heavily disguised speaker
made by Andia (Doulton & Company)
with an Amplion drive unit. Green
glazed pottery.

Fig 101 Glazed pottery speaker. The
'Bristol Auditorium Unit' made by
Bristol Potteries.

93

Fig 102 Lacquered papier mâché 'Confucius' speaker — the 'Andia'.

Fig 103 A TMC ('True Music') horn speaker with an Amplion folded horn and a Sterling Dinkie.

Fig 104 The Nesper reflex bowl speaker. The whole structure is made of lightweight metal and resembles the cone speakers in appearance and dimensions.

Fig 105 (above right) A GEC cone speaker made to have the appearance of a lamp with shade.

Fig 106 A paper cone speaker made by Sterling — the 'Melovox' with leaf pattern.

Fig 107 The Burndept 'Ethodyne' seven valve superhet.

Fig 108 A one valve regenerative receiver, model CR5 made by A.H. Grebe & Co. 1921.

Fig 109 The Federal Junior crystal set made by Federal Radio Corp. 1922.

Fig 110 Three valve regenerative receiver, model 110, made by Colin B. Kennedy Co., 1922.

Fig 111 The model V of Colin B. Kennedy Co., 1923.

Fig 112 RCA Victor Corp. of America. The portable 'Radiola II' (2-valves) Detector plus L.F. regenerative receiver. 1923.

Fig 113 This two unit system, model RA regenerative tuner and model DA detector amplifier, was made by Westinghouse for RCA. 1923.

Fig 114 The Atwater Kent Model 9 four valve TRF 'breadboard' receiver. 1924.

Fig 115 RCA Model IIIA four valve regenerative receiver. 1924.

98

Fig 116 RCA Model VIII 'portable' six valve superheterodyne set. 1924.

Fig 117 RCA model 'Radiola III' two valve regenerative set (detector, LF). 1924

99

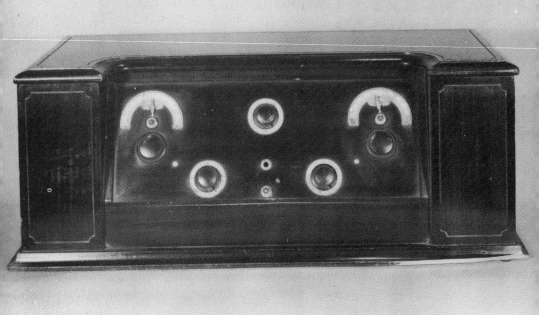

Fig 118 (above) Crosley Radio Corp. Model Trirdyn special, three valve reflex regenerative. 1924.

Fig 119 (left) Crosley Radio Corp. The 'Crosley Pup', one valve regenerative set. 1925.

Fig 120 (below) RCA Model Radiola 20 five valve TRF receiver. 1925.

Fig 121 Freed-Eisemann Radio Corp.
Model FE15 five valve TRF. 1925.

Fig 122 A.C. Dayton Co., Model XL5
five valve TRF receiver. 1925.

Fig 123 Electrical Research Labs, Model
S51, six valve reflex circuit. 1927.

Fig 124 RCA Victor Corp. of America
(Graybar Electric Co.) Model 550 five
valve TRF, AC mains set. 1929.

Fig 125 The ubiquitous 'R' valve, developed during the first world war and the mainstay for amateur constructors for several years after the war.

Fig 126 The Ediswan AR valve. In its earlier metal base form it was the first valve manufactured for amateur constructors and was introduced in 1922.

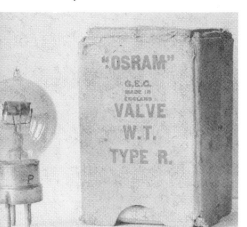

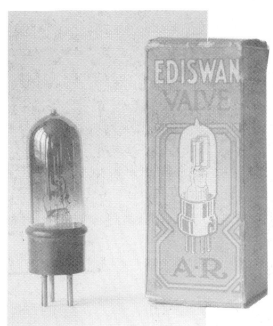

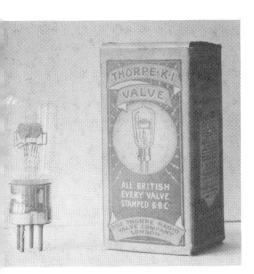

Fig 127 Introduced in 1924, the Thorpe K1 has the unusual feature of a helically wound anode.

Fig 128 Metropolitan Vickers first introduced their 'Short Path' SP55 in 1926.

103

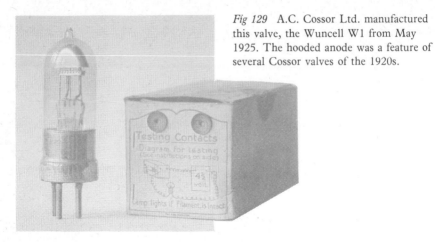

Fig 129 A.C. Cossor Ltd. manufactured this valve, the Wuncell W1 from May 1925. The hooded anode was a feature of several Cossor valves of the 1920s.

Fig 130 The BTH B5H for high frequency amplification first appeared in 1923.

Fig 131 The unique three valve set of the Loewe Radio Company, Germany. This set uses the 3NF multiple valve containing three triodes and interconnecting components in one large envelope. First appeared at Berlin Wireless Exhibition, September 1926.

Fig 132 The S625 screened grid valve marked the first successful departure from the simple triode. It was introduced by Marconi-Osram in 1927.

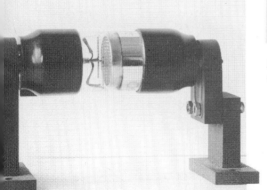

Fig 133 Marconiphone HT battery eliminator, model AC3 c1927.

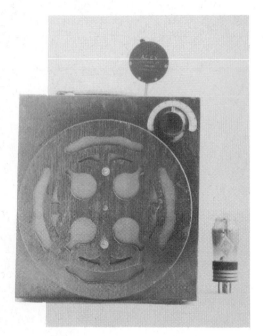

Fig 134 Portable set made by the Adey Radio Co., Ltd. in 1929. Special features: The protruding 'key' switches on HT & I.T, provides wavechange switching, contains tapped reaction coil, variable reaction coupling (by rotation); valve bases contain anode HF anode chokes.

Fig 135 & Fig 136 A novelty crystal set made in about 1926 by Kenmac Radio Ltd. This crystal set has tapped inductance tuning. It came in green or red rexine or tortoiseshell finish.

Fig 137 Another novelty crystal set, Grafton China made about 1924.

Fig 138 Another novelty crystal set, made to have the appearance of a current radio set.

Fig 139   Two more cheap novelty crystal sets

Fig 140   The lion disguises a frame aerial. The picture frame also contains a frame aerial.

Fig 141 The 'Magnora' speaker. This tortoiseshell speaker was advertised in 1923 and, although something of a 'novelty' could have been useful at the bedside.

Fig 142 The wireless theme was incorporated into glazed china seaside souvenires.

Fig 143 Cigarette cards designed to be
'instructional' on the subject of radio. A
tobacco mixture cashes in on the wireless
theme.

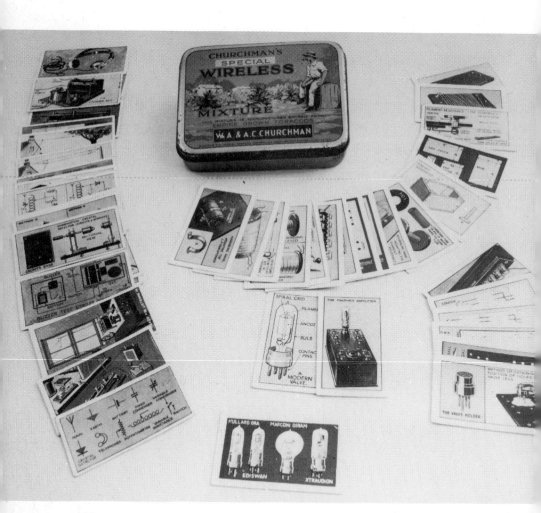

Vol. III. No. 1.   Edited by JOHN SCOTT-TAGGART, F.Inst.P., A.M.I.E.E.   June, 1924.

Fig 144 Modern Wireless was a popular magazine for the do-it-yourself enthusiast. The cover shamelessly flaunts a life-style unfamiliar to most of the magazine's readers. (June issue 1924).

111

Fig 145 The 'Wireless World' was always something of a quality magazine for the serious wireless enthusiast and still survives with an unbroken publishing record since.

Figs 146, 147 & 148 Wireless advertising of the 1920s frequently made use of ideal family settings which, with the passing years, have acquired their own innocent charm.

WHAT ARE THE AIR-WAVES SAYING?

"We were listening quietly to the wireless when he jumped up and kissed me between the Workers' Playtime and the Housewives' Choice!"

Figs 149 & 150 Seaside picture postcards have their own brand of humour which some might think was not entirley suited to the wireless theme.

Figs 151 & 152 These framed and
captioned cartoons by Albert Kaye say
something about the impact of wireless in
simple domestic situations.

Fig 153 The Ekco AD65 designed by Wells Coates and manufactured by E.K. Cole of Southend-on-Sea. 1934.

Fig 154 The Philips 2634. Three valve, AC mains TRF Moulded plastic case. This set shows strong tendency to incorporate 'brand new' design ideas. 1930.

Fig 155 The Ekco 'Consolette' Model SH25. Five valve AC/DC mains superhet. 1932. This set was first introduced in 1931 as the model RS3. It shows new design ideas and incorporates a tuning dial with station names on it.

Fig 156 The Marconiphone Model 42. Three valve AC mains TRF Veneered wood case. This was a high quality set and did not follow the current trends in design. 1932.

115

Fig 157 The Philips 'Superinductance'
63A Four Valve AC Mains TRF
veneered wood case. This well
engineered set attempted to show that
the TRF set could in fact compete with
contemporary superhets. 1933.

116

Fig 158 The Ferranti 'New Arcadia'.
Four valve AC mains superhet. Veneered
wood case. 1934.

Fig 159 The Philco 'Peoples Set' Model
444. Three valves AC/DC mains
superhet. Moulded plastic case. 1936.

118

Fig 160 The McMichael 'Duplex Four' TRF portable in leather case. This was one of the higher quality suitcase portables so popular for motoring picnics. 1932.

Fig 161 Electrical Research Labs (ERLA). Model 71. Seven Valve AC mains TRF USA 1930.

Fig 162 Philco Radio & Television Corp. Model 70, seven valve AC mains superhet (left) and Model 90, nine valve AC mains superhet (right) USA 1931.

Fig 163 Atwater Kent Mfg Co. Model 82. Seven valve C mains superhet (right) and Model 84. six valve AC mains superhet. USA 1932.

Fig 164 Zenith Radio Corp Model 805. Five valve AC mains superhet (left). Trot Mfg Co. Model 44. Four valve AC mains TRF (right) USA 1934.

Fig 165 Atwater Kent Mfg Co. Model 555 (Jewel Box) Five valve AC mains superhet. USA 1934.

Fig 166 Philco Corp. Model 89. Six valve AC mains superhet. USA 1936.

Fig 167 Zenith Radio Corp. Model 9S264. Nine valve AC mains superhet. USA 1938.

121

Appendix:
Introduction to Appendix

During the 1920s a vast number of manufacturers became involved in the new wireless industry. By the end of 1925 there were 1,716 member companies of the British Broadcasting Company. Of these, only 77 were non-manufacturing traders. The rest were involved in some aspect of manufacturing materials, components or receiving equipment. Early in 1926 the magazine *Wireless World* published a fairly comprehensive *Buyer's Guide* which listed all the companies known to be producing wireless equipment at the time. From this and one or two other contemporary sources, the following list of manufacturers has been arranged.

The name of each manufacturer is followed by the business address used at the time and this may of course be different from the manufacturing address. For each manufacturer all the wireless receivers known to have been sold by them in the early part of 1926 are listed. The name of the equipment is given where it is known and each set is given a very abbreviated description as well as its current cost.

Abbreviations used:

Ok	=	oak
Mah	=	mahogany
Wal	=	walnut
Tk	=	teak
Jac	=	Jacobean style
Open	=	Valves and other components on an exposed panel.
Enc.	=	Enclosed — a set in which doors or lids conceal the bulk of the instrument.
HF.	=	High frequency valve
Det.	=	Detector valve
LF.	=	Low frequency valve

The valve arrangement of the sets is indicated by the numbers of these valves used.

T.A.	=	tuned anode — referring to the method of tuning.
T.C.	=	transformer coupled
R.C.	=	resistance coupled
Rx	=	reflex circuit
Var	=	variometer tuned
Unk	=	unknown

Every attempt has been made to include in this list all the manufacturers known to have been making receivers in the first half of 1926. However, it is inevitable that omissions will have occurred for which the author apologises. Should readers wish to contribute information to improve the completeness of the list, the author and publishers would be extremely grateful and would endeavour to include it in subsequent editions of this book.

Concerning the price of wireless receivers in the 1920s: It is often difficult to interpret the manufacturer's quoted prices. A radio receiver could be advertised at a seemingly low price but on closer inspection would not include the cost of valves, batteries, loudspeaker, headphones, aerial and royalties. Before a set could be made to work, purchasers frequently had to spend up to twice the advertised price! The prices quoted in this list are followed by the letter 'r' meaning 'receiver only' or 'c' meaning 'complete'. This simple breakdown will however still not give the complete picture. In some cases 'complete' may mean without loudspeaker or, perhaps, with loudspeaker but without batteries. And 'receiver only' could mean with or without valves. The information given is intended to provide the most general indication to the modern student of vintage wireless who is usually well aware that a great deal of research is often necessary to establish prices and other details of any particular receiver. As the market and the fortunes of manufacturer's fluctuated so did the cost of a particular item of equipment from the time of its introduction to the time when it appeared on the 'surplus market'.

Manufacturers of Wireless Sets in 1926

Manufacturer	Equipment name	Description	Cost £	s.	d.	
Atherton & Hall The Claremont Garage General Street, Blackpool, Lancashire	Athall Radio C3	Ok, Mah. det. 2LF. TC. RC.	14.	17.	6.	r.
	Athall Radio SV4	Ok, Mah. doors. HF. det. LF.	25.	0.	0.	r.
Auriol Supplies Company 31, Leys Avenue Letchworth	Premier	Crystal set in sloping cabinet		14.	6.	r.
	Premier	ditto	1.	2.	6.	r.
	Premier	ditto	1.	5.	0.	r.
	Clearcryst	ditto		17.	6.	r.
	Auriolphone	Crystal set in enclosed cabinet.	1.	10.	0.	r.
Barnett & Soans High Street Kettering	Barsons 2	Ok, lid. det. LF. TC.	13.	5.	0.	c.
	Barsons 4	Mah. lid. det. 3LF. RC.	33.	10.	0.	c.
	Barsons 4	Jac. doors. lid. det. 3LF. RC.	38.	0.	0.	c.
	Barsons 5	Mah. lid. HF. det. 3LF. RC.	42.	10.	0.	c.
	Barsons 5	Jac. doors. lid. HF. det. 3LF. RC.	47.	0.	0.	c.
Baty, Ernest J 157, Dunstable Road Luton, Bedfordshire	The Baty Two	Unk. det. LF. DC mains.	18.	0.	0.	c.
	The Baty Four	Unk. 4v. DC mains.	42.	0.	0.	c.
Bannister & Fitton 27, Milnrow Road Rochdale	B & F	Sloping type. 1v.	4.	5.	9.	r.
		Box panel. lid. det. LF.	7.	8.	6.	r.
		Sloping panel. det. LF.	6.	6.	0.	r.
		Ok. Mah. open type. det. 2LF.	14.	3.	0.	r.
		Cabinet. det. 3LF	16.	10.	0.	r.

Company / Address	Model	Description	Price
Bates Motor Corporation 26, Coventry Street London, W1	Bates V	Leather pt. 2HF. det. 2LF.	27. 6. 0. c.
	Bates Super V	ditto	34. 13. 0. c.
Belling & Lee Limited Queensway Works Ponder's End, Middlesex		Crystal Set. Mah. box. lid.	1. 5. 0. r.
	D.C.3.	Mah. lid. det. LF. DC mains.	34. 17. 6. c.
	A.C.4.	Mah. lid. HF. det.LF. AC mains.	42. 10. 0. c.
Beard & Fitch Limited 34/36 Aylesbury Street Clerkenwell, EC1	Success	Mah. 4 & 5 v. versions. Superhet.	55 to 150 guineas.
B.S.A. Radio Limited, Small Heath, Birmingham	Models 5100, 5110, 5130	Ok. Mah. det. LF.	36. 15. 0. c.
	Models 5000, 5010, 5030	Ok. Mah. det. 2LF.	36. 15. 0 c.
BTH Company Limited Crown House Aldwych, WC2	Bijou	Crystal. wal. box. var.	1. 0. 0. r.
	Model A	Crystal. wal. box. slop. panel. lid. var.	1. 15. 0. r.
	Model VR2 form BA.	Flat top. sunk v's. det. LF.	7. 5. 0. r.
	—	Mah. Cab. doors. HF. det. LF. rx. enc. L.S.	46. 17. 6. c
	BTH portable	Leather. 3v. superhet.	26 5. 0. c.
	—	Mah. doors. lid. 6v. superhet. enc. L.S.	132. 15. 0. c.
British Engineering Products Company 570/2 Abbey House Victoria Street, SW1	Tonyphone I	Box. lid. 1v.	9. 10. 0. c.
	Tonyphone Super Two	Sloping desk. HF. det.	15. 9. 0. c.
	Tonyphone 3V	Vert. Jac. det. 2LF.	22. 10. 0. c.

Manufacturer	Equipment name	Description	Cost £ s. d.	
British & Colonial Industrialists Association Limited, 317 High Holborn, WC1	B.C.1. portable Mk.III	Mah. Folding Hexagonal Ae. HF. det. LF. TC.	18. 18. 0.	c.
British Radio Corporation Limited Elmgrove Road Weybridge, Surrey	B.R.C.	Wal. det. LF.	14. 4. 6.	c.
	B.R.C.	Wal. enclosed. det. LF.	19. 10. 0.	c.
	B.R.C.	Wal. enclosed. det. 2LF.	19. 11. 9.	c.
	B.R.C.	Wal. enclosed. HF. det. LF.	30. 13. 0.	c.
	B.R.C.	Wal. enc'd. 2HF. det. 2LF. Neutrodyne.	59. 13. 6.	c.
British Wireless Supply Company Limited 6, Blenheim Terrace Leeds	Britphone 2B	Ok. box crystal. var.	6. 6.	r.
	Britphone 3	Ok. box crystal. Cond/coil.	1. 5. 0.	r.
	Britphone 2A	Same as 2B but enclosed.	1. 2. 6.	r.
	Britphone 2E	Ok. desk. HF. det.	6. 10. 0.	r.
	Britphone 2S	Ok. flat. enc. det. LF. TC.	8. 5. 0.	r.
	Britphone 3S	Ok. enc. flat. det. 2LF. TC.	10. 7. 6.	r.
	Britphone 3S	ditto in Ok. cab with doors.	13. 7. 6.	r.
	Britphone 3Y	Ok. enc. flat. HF. det. LF. TC.	10. 7. 6.	r.
	Britphone 3Y	ditto in Ok. cab with doors.	13. 7. 6.	r.
	Britphone 4Y	Ok. enc. flat. HF. det. LF. TC.	15. 0. 0.	r.
	Britphone 4Y	ditto in Ok. cab with doors.	18. 0. 0.	r.
	Britphone 4E	Ok. desk. HF. det. 2LF.	11. 0. 0.	r.
	Britphone 4S	Ok. doors. 2HF. det. LF. 'Transatlantic'	22. 10. 0.	r.

Manufacturer	Model	Description	£	s.	d.	r./c.
Burndept Wireless Limited, Aldine House, Bedford Street, Strand, WC2	Ethophone I Mk.III	Mah. box. crystal	3.	3.	0.	r.
	Ethophone Duplex	Bak. det. LF.	6.	10.	0.	r.
	Short Wave.	Mah. det. LF.	19.	5.	0.	r.
	Ethophone Triplex	Bak. det. 2LF.	12.	11.	6.	r.
	Ethophone III Mk.III	Mah. det. 2LF.	24.	7.	6.	r.
	HF.2 Rec.	Mah. 2HF. det.	26.	17.	6.	r.
	Ethophone V Mk.IV	Mah. HF. det. 2LF.	32.	10.	0.	r.
	Ditto Mk.V	Mah. doors. ditto.	37.	10.	0.	r.
	Ethodyne	Mah. 7 valve superhet. Frame ae.	80.	12.	6.	r.
	Ethophone Grand	Mah. 2HF. det. 2LF.	78.	2.	6.	r.
Burne-Jones & Company Limited, 296, Borough High Street, London, SE1	Magnum Portable	Leather. HF. det. LF.	15.	15.	0.	c.
Burwood Limited, 41 Gt Queen Street, London, WC2	D'Accord	Ok. lid. Crystal plus 2v. rx.	11.	5.	0.	r.
	D'Accord Super 5	Mah. lid. 2HF. det. 2LF.	33.	2.	6.	r.
Butterfields Limited, Levis Motor Works, Stechford, Birmingham	Levis	Leather portable. HF. det. 2LF.	25.	0.	0.	r.
Cable Accessories Company Limited, Britannia Works, Tividale, Tipton, Staffordshire	Revophone	Mah. box with lid. crystal set. Tuned inductance	2.	10.	0.	c.
	Revophone	Mah. crystal det. plus LF.	5.	2.	6.	r.
	Revophone	Mah. 1 valve	4.	2.	6.	r.
	Revophone	Mah. det. LF.	9.	5.	0.	c.

127

128

Manufacturer	Equipment name	Description	Cost £	s.	d.	
	Revophone III	Mah. det. 2LF.	11	17.	6.	c.
	Revophone 4662	Ok. Jac. HF. det. 2LF.	40.	10.	0.	c.
	4666	Mah. cab. ditto.	41.	10.	0.	c.
	4664	Ok. Jac. pedestal ditto.	58.	0.	0.	c.
	4668	Mah. pedestal. ditto.	60.	10.	0.	c.
C.A.C. Radio Limited 10, Rangoon Street London, EC3	C.A.C. portable.	Leather. HF. det. 2LF.	25.	4.	0.	c.
C.A.V. (C.A. Vandervell & Company Limited) Acton, London W3	C.A.V. portable.	Leather. 3v. folded horn L.S.	21.	17.	6.	c.
	C.A.V. Baby Grand.	Ok. Mah. pedestal. det. 2LF. enc. L.S.	26.	17.	6.	c.
Cahill & Company Limited 64 Newman Street London, W1	Pelican	Mah. det only. portable	10.	0.	0.	c.
	Pelican	Mah. portable det. 2LF.	20.	0.	0.	c.
	Pelican	Mah. portable HF. det. 2LF.	32.	10.	0.	c.
	Pelican	Mah. portable 2HF. det. 2LF.	40.	0.	0.	c.
Carpax Company Limited, 312, Deansgate, Manchester	Carpax Logodyne Five	Mah. sloping panel. 2HF. det. 2LF.	28.	10.	0.	c.
Climax Radio Electric Limited Quill Works, Putney London, SW15	Climax Monovalve.	Ok. 1 valve portable	10.	4.	0.	c.

Manufacturer / Address	Model	Description	£	s.	d.	
City Radio Service, 226 Warwick Road, Greet, Birmingham	Warwick No.1.	Ok. box with lid. Crystal.	1.	6.	0.	c.
Colbery & Company Limited, C.T., 8 St. James Walk, London, EC1	Ideal V3	Leather. Portable. det. 2LF.	22.	10.	0.	c.
Collins & John Limited, 52 Hatton Gardens, London, EC1, Also at: 9/10 Tenby Street, Birmingham	Amplex Model A	Ok. Mah. enc. crystal	1.	9.	0.	r.
	Amplex Model B	Open panel crystal		15.	0.	r.
	Amplex Model C	Same as A but with 5XX coils.	1.	17.	6.	r.
	Amplex 5XX	Ok. encl. crystal for 5XX only.	1.	0.	0.	r.
	Amplex A.V.	Ok. Mah. Crystal plus 1v.	3.	17.	6.	r.
	Amplex	Open panel 1v.	3.	12.	6.	r.
	Amplex-Reinartz	ditto	4.	17.	6.	r.
	Amplex Roll Top	Ok. Mah. Roll Top. 1v.	6.	2.	6.	r
	Amplex	Ok. Mah. Roll Top. det. 2LF.	14.	12.	6.	r.
Corrall, A.J., 226 Warwick Road, Greet, Birmingham	Warwick IV	Ok. 1v.	7.	0.	0.	r.
Curtis Limited, Peter, 75A Camden Road, London, NW1	Radionette	Ok. encl. Crystal	1.	5.	0.	r.
	Duodyne II	Tk. open. det. LF.	8.	15.	0.	r.
	Duodyne II	Tk. encl. doors. det. LF.	11.	15.	0.	r.
	Duodyne III regenerative	Tk. open. det. 2LF.	11.	17.	6.	r
	ditto	Tk. encl. doors. ditto.	15.	7.	6.	r.
	Duodyne III HF	Tk. open 2HF. det.	11.	17.	6.	r.

Manufacturer	Equipment name	Description	Cost £	s.	d.	
	Duodyne III HF	Tk. encl. doors. ditto.	15.	7.	6.	r.
	Duodyne portable IV	Mah. encl. HF. det. 2LF.	21.	0.	0.	c.
	ditto	Leather. ditto.	22.	0.	0.	c.
	Duodyne V	Tk. Open. 2HF. det. 2LF.	21.	2.	6.	r.
	ditto	Tk. encl. doors. ditto	25.	12.	6.	r.
	Curtis	Various cabs. 8v. superhet.	44 to 75 guineas.			c.
	Curtis portable	Tk. Ok. 8v. superhet.	56.	5.	0.	c.
Dargue Brothers Limited	Simplon	Box Crystal	1.	10.	0.	c.
	Simplon No.2	ditto with lid.	2.	5.	0.	c.
Simplon Technical Instrument Works Halifax, Yorkshire	Simplon	Encl. Sloping panel det. LF.	8.	7.	6.	r.
	Simplon Autodyne II	Table cab. det. LF.	10.	0.	0.	r.
	Simplon Autodyne III	Table cab. det. 2LF.	23.	5.	6.	c.
	Simplon ditto	Ok. Mah. Pedestal. ditto.	29.	4.	0.	c.
	Simplon IV	Ok. Mah. lid. doors. 4v. Neutrodyne.	47.	10	0.	c.
	Simplon	Mah. pedestal. HF. det. 2LF.	35.	7.	6.	c.
Dunham, C.S.	C.S.D.31.	Crystal set. Ok. Mah.	1.	5.	0.	r.
234/236 Brixton Hill London, SW2	C.S.D.37.	1 valve	3.	5.	0.	r.
	C.S.D.58.	Open. det. LF.	5.	17.	6.	r.
	C.S.D.42.	Desk. HF. det.	8.	15.	0.	r.
	C.S.D.48.	Cabinet. HF. det.	10.	18.	0.	r.
	C.S.D.45.	Ok. Mah. desk. doors. HF. det. LF.	12.	8.	0.	r.
	C.S.D.51D.	Ok. Mah. cab. doors. HF. det. LF.	15.	16.	0.	r.
	C.S.D.57.	Ok. Mah. doors. 4v.	27.	10.	0.	r.
	C.S.D.56.	Ok. Mah. sloping panel. 4v.	18.	10.	0.	r.

Maker / Address	Model	Description	£	s	d	
Dynametry Mains Supply Staines	3V Mains	3 valve DC mains set.	30.	0.	0.	c.
	4V Mains	4 valve DC mains set.	38.	0.	0.	c.
Eagle Engineering Company Limited Eagle Works Warwick	Chakophone No.3A	Box, lid. Crystal set	2.	0.	0.	r.
	Chakophone No.4	Open box. Crystal.	1.	10.	0.	r.
	Chakophone No.1	Open box. 1 valve.	3.	12.	6.	r.
	Chakophone No.5a	Box cab. lid. 1 valve	5.	0.	0.	r.
	Chakophone No.11	Ok. 'Salt box' lid. 1 valve	5.	17.	6.	r.
	Chakophone No.2 2V	Mah. Sloping desk. HF. det. (also kit form)				
	Chakophone Super No.9.	Mah. vert panel. det. LF.	6.	17.	6.	r.
	Chakophone No.7. 2V	Mah. vert panel. 2v.	8.	15.	0.	r.
	Chakophone No.9.	Ok. cab. det. LF.	12.	3.	0.	r.
	Chakophone No.2. 3V	Mah. slop.desk. HF. det. LF. (also kit form)	6.	15.	0.	r.
	Chakophone No.1B	Ok. cab. doors. det. 2LF.	8.	17.	6.	r.
	Chakophone No.7. 3V	Mah. ver. panel. HF. det. LF.	11.	17.	6.	r.
	De Luxe Pedestal	Ok. encl. L.S. HF. det. 2LF.	15.	0.	6.	r.
	Chakophone No.2. 4V	Mah. slop.desk. HF. det. 2LF. (also kit form)	35.	10.	0.	r.
	Chakophone No.7. 4V	Vert. panel doors. HF. det. 2LF.	10.	17.	6.	r.
	ditto	ditto no doors	21.	18.	0.	r.
			18.	13.	0.	r.
Edison Swan Electric Company Limited 123/5 Queen Victoria Street London, EC4	Ediswan WL1924 Short wave.	Mah. Crystal set. Flat.	1.	18.	4.	c.
	WL1924 L Long wave	ditto	2.	0.	10.	c.
	WL1924 P (for high power stn.)	Crystal set.	1	0.	0.	r.
	WL 217	Crystal-valve set. (HF. cryst. det.) Flat.	10.	12.	9.	c.

Manufacturer	Equipment name	Description		Cost £ s. d.			
	Toovee	Mah. vert. panel., 2v. rx.		18.	5.	0.	c.
	Compactum	Moulded. det. LF.		11.	11.	0.	c.
	Toovee portable	Mah. doors. same as toovee above.		16.	5.	0.	c.
	Long-range Radiophone	Mah. doors. HFrx. det. 2LF.		33.	0.	0.	c.
Electrical Accessories Manufacturing Company Progress Works Low Hall Mills Holbeck, Leeds	Type 2B Crystal set	Jacobean Oak		1.	5.	0.	r.
	Prento D1.	Flat Oak case. 1 valve.		3.	17.	6.	r.
	Prento F2	Flat Walnut. HF., Det.		6.	10.	0.	r.
	Prento D2	Flat Oak case. Det., LF.		6.	5.	0.	r.
	Prento F3.	Flat walnut. HF. Det. LF.		9.	7.	6.	r.
	Prento C.B.3 & C.3	Cabinet Oak. ditto		12.	17.	6.	r.
	Prento 3D.2	Cabinet with doors, Oak. ditto		15.	17.	6.	r.
	Prento 3D.4	ditto		20.	17.	6.	r.
	Prento D3	Flat Oak case. Det., 2LF.		10.	7.	0.	r.
	Prento F.4	Flat Walnut HF., Det., 2LF.		13.	10.	0.	r.
	Prento C.B.4	Cabinet, Oak. ditto		19.	10.	0.	r.
	Prento C.4	ditto		16.	10.	0.	r.
	Prento 4D.2	ditto with doors		21.	0.	0.	r.
	Prento 4D.4	ditto		27.	0.	0.	r.
Elliott, C.L. 12, Queen's Road London, SW8	Volutone	Oak. 1 valve set.	from	2.	10.	0.	r.
	Volutone	Oak. Det., LF.	from	4.	4.	0.	r.
	Volutone	Oak. Det., 2LF.	from	6.	6.	0.	r.
	Volutone	Oak. HF., Det. LF.	from	5.	5.	0.	r.
	Volutone	Oak. HF., Det., 2LF.	from	10.	10.	0.	r.

	Model	Description	£	s.	d.	
Emsco Radio	Emsco 1	Unknown appearance. Det., LF.	13.	0.	0.	c.
24 Leytonstone Road	Emsco 2	ditto HF., Det.	10.	0.	0.	c.
London, E15	Emsco 3	ditto HF., Det., LF.	20.	0.	0.	c.
	Emsco 4	ditto Det., 2LF.	20.	0.	0.	c.
	Emsco 5	ditto HF., Det., 2LF.	30.	0.	0.	c.
	Emsco 6	ditto 4 valve reflex neutrodyne.	32.	0.	0.	c.
Engineering Works (Electrical & General) Limited	Rayol 2V	Jacobean fumed oak. glass panel. HF., Det. Tun.A.	10.	14.	0.	r.
17/21 Thurlow Park Road	Rayol 3V	ditto HF., Det., LF. Tuned anode.				
West Dulwich	Radio-Pal	Crocodile leatherette. HF., Det., 2LF.	22.	9.	0.	c.
	Radio-Pal de Luxe	Solid leather. HF., Det., 2LF.	27.	14.	0.	c.
Ericsson Manufacturing Company Limited, British L.M.	0/1002 Crystal set	Oak case with lid. 300-700 metres.	1.	1.	0.	r.
67/73 Kingway	0/1050 Miniature, crystal.	Turned polished ebonite. 300-500 metres.		7.	6.	r.
London WC2	0/1001	Walnut box, HF., Det., TA.	7.	10.	0.	r.
	0/1005	Sloping panel. HF., Det., TA.	7.	15.	0.	r.
	0/1082 Family set.	Oak, folding doors. Det., LF. TC.	8.	15.	0.	r.
	0/1003	Sloping panel. HF., Det., LF. TC. TA.	14.	0.	0.	r.
	0/1083	Mahog. folding doors. HF., Det., LF., TC., TA.	20.	0.	0.	r.
	0/1041	Queen Anne style. Ok., Mah., or Wal. HF., Det., 2LF.	77.	10.	0.	r.
	0/1084	Mah. folding doors & drawer. HF., Det., 2LF.	30.	0.	0.	r.

Manufacturer	Equipment name	Description	Cost £	s.	d.	
Excelsior Motor Company Limited King's Road, Tyseley Birmingham	Excelphone	Sloping panel, Mah. HF., Det. 2LF.	28.	10.	–. 0.	c.
Fairbrother, John 94 Prescot Road Liverpool	Fair-Fal	Mah. box. One valve	6.	5.	0.	c.
	Fair-Fal	Mah. folding doors. Det., LF.	13.	0.	0.	c.
	Fair-Fal	Mah. folding doors. HF., Det., LF.	17.	10.	0.	c.
	Fair-Fal	Mah. folding doors. H., Det., 2LF.	25.	0.	0.	c.
Falk, Stadelmann & Company Limited 83/93 Farringdon Road London, EC1	Efescaphone Benbow	Crystal set. Mah. enclosed.	2.	1.	0.	r.
	Efescaphone St. Vincent	Mah. oblong. Valve crystal reflex.	5.	12.	6.	r.
	Efescaphone Seymour	Oak with sliding shutter. Det., LF.	11.	15.	0.	r.
	Efescaphone Nelson	Mah. roll front. HF., Det., LF.	22.	17.	6.	r.
	Efescaphone Rodney	Wal. sloping front HF., Det., LF.	15.	17.	6	r.
	Efescaphone Hood	Wal. square. HF., Det., LF.	13.	17.	6.	r.
	Efescaphone Nelson	Mah. roll front. HF., Det., 2LF.	32.	10.	0.	r.
Fallowfield Limited, J. 61/62 Newman Street London, W1	Corner Cabinet	Oak. HF., Det., LF.	63.	0.	0.	c.
Fellows Magneto Company Limited	Fellocryst Super	Oak case. Crystal Set.	1.	15.	0.	c.
	Fellophone Super One	Leatherette box. One valve.	4.	17.	6.	c.

Firm / Address	Model	Description	£	s.	d.	
Cumberland Avenue Park Royal London, NW10	Little Giant	Leatherette box. Det., LF.	6.	15.	0.	c.
	Fellophone Super 3	Sloping Mah. HF., Det., LF.	10.	5.	0.	c.
	Fellophone portable 3	Leatherette case. HF., Det., LF. Reflex	12.	0.	0.	c.
	Fellophone Grand 3	Oak or Sheraton folding doors. HF., Det., LF.	14.	10.	0.	c.
	Fellophone Super 5	Oak folding doors. HF., Det., 3LF., (1 TC., 2 RC.)	24.	0.	0.	c.
	Fellophone Jacobean 5	Oak Bureau. ditto.	50.	0.	0.	c.
Flinders (Wholesale) Limited 18 Butt Road and Essex Street, Colchester	Flinderphone	Crystal set.	1.	7.	6.	r.
	Flinderphone	One valve set.	5.	0.	0.	r.
	Flinderphone Super 2	Two valve set. Det., LF.	6.	10.	0.	r.
		Ditto with all accessories inc. speaker.	11.	1.	6.	c.
Fraser & Glass Assembly Works Middle Lane Hornsey, London, N8	Fortevex Junior. Model 1	Crystal set. Moulded base		6.	0.	r.
	Fortevex Junior. Model 2	Crystal set. Moulded base		7.	6.	r.
Fuller's United Electric Works Limited Woodland Works Chadwell Heath, Essex	Sparta	Four valve set. HF., Det., 2LF.	19.	6.	0.	r.
Gambrell Brothers Limited 76 Victoria Street London, SW1	The Gambrell Cabinet 2	Mah. folding doors. Det., LF.	15.	0.	0.	r.
	The Gambrell Baby two	Mah. box. Det., LF.	8.	0.	0.	r.
	The Gambrell Baby Grand	Mah. cabinet. Det., LF. DC mains	17.	0.	0.	r.

Manufacturer	Equipment name		Description	Cost £	s.	d.	
	The Gambrell Cabinet 3		Mah. cabinet folding doors. Det., 2LF.	21.	17.	6.	r.
	ditto	3A	ditto HF., Det., LF.	25.	17.	6.	r.
	ditto	3B	ditto ditto	29.	15.	0.	r.
	The Gambrell Cabinet 4		ditto HF., Det., 2LF.	30.	10.	0.	r.
	ditto	4A	ditto ditto	32.	10.	0.	r.
General Electric Company Limited Magnet House, Kingsway, London W.C.2.	Junior		Mah. Open, flat top crystal set.	2.	16.	0.	r.
	No.1.		Mah. box with lid. Crystal set.	5.	5.	0.	r.
	Gecophone B.C.3000		Mah. upright box. One valve.	5.	0.	0.	r.
	ditto B.C.3001, 3050, 3051		Versions of B.C.3000 with various accessories. Up to:	7.	16.	0.	c.
	Gecophone B.C.3250		Mah. flat top. Det. LF.	8.	12.	0.	r.
	ditto B.C.3251, 3260, 3266		Versions of B.C.3250 with various accessories. Up to:	13.	0.	0.	c.
	Gecophone B.C.3220		Mah. Smokers cab. doors. Det. LF.	11.	15.	0.	r.
	ditto B.C.3200, 3205		Versions of B.C.3220 with various accessories. Up to:	15;	15;	0.	c.
	Gecophone B.C.2000		Mah. Smokers cab. doors. HF., Det.	11.	15.	0.	r.
	ditto B.C.2001/2/3		Versions of B.C.2000 with various accessories. Up to:	15.	10.	0.	c.
	Gecophone B.C.3350		Mah. upright box. Det., 2LF.	19.	2.	6.	r.
	ditto B.C.3351, 3355, 3356		Versions of B.C.3350 with various accessories. Up to:	23.	9.	6.	c.

Model	Description	£	s.	d.	
Gecophone B.C.3301	Mah. cabinet with doors. Det. 2LF.	20.	2.	6.	r.
ditto B.C.3300, 3306, 3305	Versions of B.C.3301 with various accessories. Up to:	25.	17.	6.	c.
Gecophone B.C.4000	Mah. table model. HF., Det., 2LF.	30.	0.	0.	r.
ditto B.C.4020, 4001, 4021	Versions of B.C.4000 with various accessories. Up to:	37.	5.	0.	c.
Gecophone B.C.4444	Mah. Cabinet with integral speaker. HF., Det., 2LF.	60.	0.	0.	c.
Gecophone B.C.2010	ditto de Luxe Model	85.	0.	0.	c.
Gecophone B.C.3400	Combination of B.C.2001 plus 2 stage amplifier B.C.2580	29.	10.	0.	c.
Gecophone B.C.2050	Mah. table model. doors. HF., Det., 3LF.	36.	2.	6.	r.
Gecophone B.C.2051	ditto with accessories	44.	7.	6.	c.
Gecophone B.C.6000	Mah. table model. 6 valve superhet	52.	10.	0.	c.
Gecophone B.C.8800	Mah. table model. 8 valve superhet	73.	10.	0.	c.
General Radio Company Limited, 235 Regent Street, London, W1					
G.R.C.6.	Crystal set. Ok. box.	2.	10.	0.	r.
G.R.C.501	Box type one valve	9.	0.	0.	r.
Type 15	Wal. with front panel. Det. LF.	6.	15.	0.	r.
Type 53	Teak portable. HF., Det., LF.	18.	0.	0.	c.
Gent & Company Limited, Faraday Works, Leicester					
Tangent Radiomatic D	Tk or Ok. Det., LF.	8.	5.	0.	r.
Tangent Radiomatic B	Supplied without cabinet. HF., Det., LF.	17.	7.	6.	r.
Tangent Radiomatic B	ditto HF., Det., 2LF.	22.	5.	0.	r.
Gisbornes, 28/32 Longmore Street, Birmingham					
II	Ok. folding doors. Det., LF.	10.	5.	0.	c.
Silvertone	Portable, rexine. 2 cases. Det., LF.	15.	0.	0.	c.
III	Ok. folding doors. Det., 2LF.	12.	10.	0.	c.

Manufacturer	Equipment name	Description	Cost £	s.	d.	
Gladwell & Kell Limited 258 Gray's Inn Road London WC1	Liquitone	Mah. cabinet. HF., Det., LF.	25.	4.	6.	r.
		ditto complete with all accessories	35.	0.	0.	c.
Graham & Company, R.F. Norbex Works 101, Gloucester Road Kingston-upon-Thames Surrey	Broadwood-Graham	Floor model self contained HF., Det., LF.	68.	10.	0.	c.
Gilfillan Brothers Limited 63 High Holborn London WC1	Gillan Ubique	Leather cased portable HF., Det., LF.	23.	3.	0.	c.
	Gillan Ubique A	ditto but no speaker	18.	18.	0.	r.
Halcyon Wireless Supply Company Limited 110 Knightsbridge London WC1	Halcyon	Ok. cabinet. four valve portable	25.	0.	0.	c.
	Halcyon	ditto five valve portable	33.	2.	6.	c.
Hart Collins Limited 38a Bessborough Street London SW1	Hart Collins	Ok. or leatherette. 4 valve portable	26.	18.	0.	c.
Henderson & Company Limited, W.J. 351 Fulham Road London SW10	B.R.C.1	Box type crystal set	1.	12.	6.	r.
	B.R.C.1A	ditto	1.	19.	0.	r.
	B.R.1	One valve set.	4.	0.	0.	r.
	B.R.2	Two valve set. Det., LF.	6.	5.	0.	r.

Model	Description	£	s.	d.	
H.R.2A	Two valve set. HF., Det.	9.	15.	0.	r.
H.R.3A	Vertical panel type. HF., Det., LF.	15.	0.	0.	r.
H.R.4A	Ok. or Mah. HF., Det., 2LF.	20.	0.	0.	r.
Hirst Brothers & Company Limited					
Tameside R.535	Ok. open type. Crystal set. sliding coil tuned.		10.	0.	r.
Tameside R.542	ditto variometer tuned	1.	2.	6.	r.
Tameside R.424	Ok. open desk type. Cond. tuned	1.	5.	0.	r.
Tameside R.545	Ok. hinged lid. Cond. or Variometer tuned	1.	10.	0.	r.
Tameside R.1000	Ok. upright panel. one valve	3.	2.	6.	r.
Tameside R.365	Ok. desk sloping panel. one valve	1.	12.	0.	r.
Tameside R.1011	Ok. upright panel. HF., Det., TA.	6.	5.	0.	r.
Tameside R.1011B	ditto Ae. reaction	6.	5.	0.	r.
Tameside R.1147 de Luxe	Ok. upright panel, doors. HF., Det., TA.	11.	5.	0.	r.
Tameside R.430	Ok. desk sloping panel. HF., Det., TA.	5.	15.	0.	r.
Tameside R.555	Ok. enclosed, doors. HF., Det., TA.	11.	5.	0.	r.
Tameside R.1013	Ok. Upright panel. HF., Det., LF., TA., TC.	9.	17.	6.	r.
Tameside R.1013B	ditto but with aerial reaction.	9.	17.	6.	r.
Tameside R.1148 de Luxe	Ok. upright panel, doors. HF., Det., LF., TA.	13.	7.	6.	r.
Tameside R.419	Ok. desk sloping panel. HF., Det., LF., TA.	8.	17.	6.	r.
Tameside R.1016	Ok. upright panel. HF., Det., 2LF., TA., 2TC.	13.	10.	0.	r.
Tameside R.1149 de Luxe	Ok. upright, doors. ditto	16.	0.	0.	r.

Manufacturer	Equipment name	Description	Cost £	s.	d.	
	Tameside R.437	Ok. desk sloping panel. ditto	11.	0.	0.	r.
	Tameside R.444	Ok. table, hinged lid, doors. ditto	24.	10.	0.	r.
Holrose Manufacturing Company 43 Lonsdale Road Kilburn London NW6	The Holrose	Crystal set in leatherette case.		8.	6.	r.
Hough Limited, J.E. Edison Bell Works 62 Glengall Road Peckham London SE15	Crystal valve	Ok. desk. crystal det. One valve dual (Hf. or LF.)	7.	19.	6.	r.
	ditto	Mahogany. ditto	8.	7.	6.	r.
	Crystal 2-valve	Ok. or Mah. Crystal det. 2 valves reflex.	10.	14.	0.	r.
	ditto	Jacobean, doors. On pedestal	17.	0.	0.	r.
	Crystal 3-valve	Desk pattern, open. Crystal det. 3 valves reflex.	13.	2.	6.	r.
	Bijou	Desk type with dust flap. Det., LF.	5.	0.	0.	r.
Igna Engineering Company Limited 99 High Street, Dudley	Ignaphone	Crystal set in leatherette case.		8.	6.	r.
Johnson, Thomas T. 17/19 Catherine Street Salisbury	Sarumphone	Mah. box crystal set.		15.	6.	r.
	Sarumphone	Mah. cabinet, doors, lid, drawers. HF., Det.	10.	0.	0.	c.

Manufacturer / Address	Model	Description	£	s	d	
	Sarumphone	ditto HF., Det., LF.	16.	0.	0.	c.
	Sarumphone	Mah. cabinet, doors. HF., Det., 3LF.	26.	0.	0.	c.
King Quality Products Incorporated 27/28 Anning Street London WC2	King 10S.K.	Mah. Table, lid. 2HF., Det., LF. Neutrodyne	26.	0.	0.	r.
	King Model 25	ditto 2HF., Det., 2LF. Neutrodyne	32.	0.	0.	r.
	King Model 25S	ditto with Amplion speaker incorporated.	55.	0.	0.	c.
Knight Limited, A.W. 167 Rye Lane Peckham	Kaynite (late Dulcivox)	Sloping panel. One valve reflex. single knob.	7.	15.	0.	r.
	Kaynite ditto	Sloping panel. Two valve reflex. single knob.	9.	17.	0.	r.
Lamplugh Limited, S.A. King's Road Tyseley Birmingham	No.1030	Ok. cabinet crystal set. Variometer	1.	10.	0.	r.
	No.1052 Junior	Moulded ebonite crystal set. Sliding coil.		9.	6.	r.
	No.1018	Ok. cabinet crystal set. Var. With all accessories	4.	4.	0.	c.
	Lamplugh Desk	Ok. sloping panel. HF., Det.	7.	15.	0.	r.
	Lamplugh Popular.	Flat top for use with LS., Det., LF.	6.	12.	6.	r.
	Lamplugh 1078	Ok. HF., Det., LF.	18.	7.	6.	r.
	Lamplugh Desk	Ok. Sloping panel. HF., Det., 2LF.	17.	10.	0.	r.
Lissen Limited Lissenium Works Friars Lane Richmond, Surrey	Lissen	Crystal set.		10.	0.	r.

Manufacturer	Equipment name	Description	Cost £	s.	d.	
Liver Radio Manufacturing Company Limited 30, Islington Liverpool	Liverphone	Ok. or Mah. Sloping panel. Crystal set. Var.	1.	5.	0.	r.
	ditto	ditto	2.	0.	0.	c.
	Liverphone	Sloping panel. Det., LF.	7.	5.	0.	r.
	Liverphone	Sloping panel. Det., 2LF.	12.	15.	0.	r.
	Liverphone	Enclosed cabinet. Four valves. Up to:	22.	10.	0.	r.
McMichael Limited, L. Wexham Road Slough Buckinghamshire	B.R.2	Mah. cabinet. HF., Det. TA.	16.	15.	0.	r.
	B.R.2A	Mah. cabinet. Det., LF. TA.	11.	5.	0.	r.
	B.R.3	Mah. cabinet. HF., Det., LF.	19.	17	6.	r.
	Standard de Luxe	Mah. cabinet, doors. HF., Det., 2LF.	35.	10.	0.	r.
	Neutrodyne	Mah. cabinet on plinth. 4-valve neutrodyne.	18.	5.	0.	r.
	Superhet	Mah. cabinet. Superheterodyne.	25.	16.	6.	r.
M.A.P. Company Great Lister Street Birmingham	M.A.P. Crystal	Aluminium. crystal set.	1.	7.	6.	r.
	M.A.P. Minor	Mah. totally enclosed vertical. Det., LF.	12.	15.	0.	c.
	M.A.P. Major	Mah. ditto HF., Det., 2LF.	24.	10.	0.	c.
Marconiphone Company Limited 210/212 Tottenham Court Road, London, W1	Universal Baby	Moulded Crystal set. Var.	1.	7.	0.	r.
	V.1	Mah. upright panel, lid. One valve	9.	7.	8.	c.
	V.2A Long Range	Mah. Wal. or Tk. Enclosed cabinet. 2-valve reflex.	15.	16.	2.	c.

		£	s.	d.	
ditto Portable	ditto fitted with valves suitable for dry batteries.	17.	8.	0.	c.
Type 21	Mah. upright. Det., LF.	13.	4.	6.	c.
V.3A	Mah. Enclosed cabinet. 3-valve reflex.	33.	18.	8.	c.
Type 31	Mah. cabinet, lid. Det., 2LF.	21.	15.	6.	c.
V.4B	Mah. upright cabinet. Doors. HF., Det., 2LF.	56.	5.	6.	c.
Type 41	ditto	37.	19.	0.	c.
Type 81 'Straight 8'	Mah. sloping panel. 5HF., Det., 2LF., Neutrodyne.	67.	16.	0.	c.
The Sterling range:					
R.1550	Crystal set. Wal. Var. 'Semi-automatic' crystal	3.	3.	0.	c.
Anodion R.1560	Wal. desk. One valve.	11.	3.	4.	c.
Anodion R.1572	Wal. hinged desk top. Det., LF.	14.	14.	4.	c.
Long Range Anodion R.1565	ditto HF., Det.	14.	11.	6.	c.
Long Range R.1588	Mah. cabinet, doors. HF., Det.	18.	11.	0.	c.
Anodion R.1584	Mah. desk, hinged lid. Det., 2LF.	24.	14.	5.	c.
Anodion R.1605	Wal. cabinet, doors, battery plinth. Det., 2LF.	36.	0.	1.	c.
Threeflex	Wal. cabinet, doors. Frame ae. Crystal + 3-valves reflex.	29.	7.	6.	c.
Anodion R.1578 'Long Range'	Wal. desk top, hinged lid. HF., Det., LF.	22.	13.	4.	c.
Anodion R.1610 'Long Range'	Wal. desk top, hinged lid. HF., Det., 2LF.	30.	19.	7.	c.
Long Range R.1615	Wal. cabinet, doors, battery plinth. HF., Det., 2LF.	43.	4.	7.	c.

Manufacturer	Equipment name	Description	£	Cost s.	d.	
	Regina R.1618	Ok. Floor model. Primax speaker. HF., Det., 2LF.	65.	10.	0.	c.
	Imperial R.1619	Mah. ditto	74.	10.	0.	c.
	R.1620	Wal. Floor cabinet. Primax speaker. HF., Det., 2LF.	98.	10.	0.	c.
	R.1621	Wal. Floor cabinet. Folded horn speaker. ditto.	122.	10.	0.	c.
Master Radio Manufacturing Company 30 Rosamond Street East All Saints Manchester	Master Junior	Mah. Crystal set. Open type detector.		7.	6.	r.
	Mastavox	Mah. Crystal set. Dust proof detector.		8.	6.	r.
Metropolitan Vickers 'Metro-Vick Supplies Limited' 4 Central Buildings Westminster London SW1	Cosmos	Moulded, round base. Crystal set. Var. cond. tuning.	1.	5.	0.	r.
	Cosmos 'Baby Grand'	Moulded, round base. Crystal/valve det., 2LF. RC.	14.	10.	0.	c.
	ditto	version without crystal. Approx:	15.	0.	0.	c.
	Cosmos Universal VS6	Various cases. Reflex, det., 3LF. RC. Up to:	30.	10.	0.	r.
	Cosmos Universal VS7	Various cases. ditto + built-in speaker. Up to:	63.	0.	0.	r.
Midland Radiotelephone	Mellowtone 2	Ok. or Mah. Flat. Det., LF.	8.	12.	6.	r.

Model	Description	£	s.	d.	
Mellowtone 3	Various cabinets. HF., Det., LF.	Up to: 31.	17.	6.	r.
Mellowtone 4	ditto HF.Dett., 2LF.	Up to: 37.	10.	0.	r.
Mellowtone 5	ditto 2HF., Det., 2LF.	Up to: 43.	2.	6.	r.
Mellowtone 6	ditto 2HF., Det., 3LF.	Up to: 73.	13.	0.	r.
Motorists' Purchasing Association Limited 62 Conduit Street London W1					
The M.P.A. Inclusive Three	Ok. Jacobean portable. Det., 2LF.	19.	19.	0.	c.
The M.P.A. Super Portable	Honduras Mah. 2HF., Det., 2LF.	34.	2.	6.	c.
The M.P.A. Portable de Luxe	ditto 2HF., Det., 3LF.	42.	15.	0.	c.
Standard Table Model	Mah. cabinet, doors. HF., Det., LF.	27.	7.	6.	c.
Super 5 'Constructors'	Five valve kit with diagrams.	14.	14.	0.	r.
Em-pe-a-dyne	Mah. carved cabinet. 5-valves	48.	2.	6.	c.
National Wireless & Electric Company (R.R. Goding Limited) 42 Gray's Inn Road London WC1					
Gnat N.Mk.CI.	Crystal set	1.	1.	0.	r.
Gnat N.Mk.CL.	Mah. with lid. Crystal set.	1.	12.	6.	r.
Gnat N.Mk.CX.	Mah. with lid. Crystal set.	2.	2.	6.	r.
N.Mk.1*	Mah. One valve	5.	5.	0.	r.
N.Mk.1* de Luxe	Mah. with glass. One valve	6.	15.	0.	r.
N.Mk.2*	Mah. Det., LF., TC.	8.	10.	0.	r.
N.Mk.2* de Luxe	Mah. glass doors. Det., LF., TC.	10.	10.	0.	r.
N.Mk.3 Portable	Mah. Det., 2LF., TC.	11.	17.	6.	r.
N.Mk.3*	Mah. Det., 2LF., TC.	12.	10.	0.	r.
N.Mk.3* de Luxe	Mah. glass doors. Det., 2LF., TC.	14.	10.	0.	r.
N.Mk.4* de Luxe	Mah. HF., Det., 2LF.	28.	5.	0.	r.

Manufacturer	Equipment name	Description	£	s.	d.	
Neutron Limited Sentinel House Southampton Row London WC1	Neutron Biltin	Mah. with built-in Amplion LS., Det, LF.	16.	17.	6.	c.
Non-Aerial Wireless Manufacturing Company 181 Shaftesbury Avenue London WC2	N-A Portable D Type	Mah. with built-in Sterling 'Dinkie' LS., Det, 2LF.	23.	2.	0.	c.
	N-A Portable C Type	ditto without LS.	18.	18.	0.	c.
Ormsby & Company, L. 28 Page Street Westminster London SW1	Ormsby	Mah. lid. Det., LF.	9.	10.	0.	r.
	Ormsby	ditto & inc. LS.	15.	0.	0.	c.
	Ormsby	Mah. lid. 3-valve reflex. inc. LS.	18.	7.	6.	c.
	Ormsby	Mah. 4-valve set. inc. Amplion A.R.19, LS.	39.	10.	0.	c.
Prince's Electric Clocks Limited 173 New Bond Street London W1	Princeps Concert Receivers	Mah. or Ok. Cabinet. Jacobean 4-valves	27.	10.	0.	c.
	ditto	ditto but in burr walnut	29.	0.	0.	c.
Radio-Arc Electrical Company Limited Bennett Street Chiswick, London W4	Liberty Ironclad	Iron cased crystal set.	6.	16.	6.	r.
	Liberty Short-Wave	Ok. or Mah. Det., LF.	6.	0.	0.	r.
	Liberty	Ok. or Mah. 6-valve superhet.	32.	5.	0.	r.
	Liberty	Ok. or Mah. 8-valve superhet.	38.	10.	0.	r.

Company	Model	Description	£	s.	d.	
Radio Communication Company Limited 34/35 Norfolk Street London WC2	Polar	Oak box sloping panel Crystal set.	1.	7.	6.	r.
	Polar Twin	Crystalline metal cabinet. Det., LF.	6.	15.	0.	r.
	Polar Twin	Oak cabinet. Det., LF.	8.	2.	6.	r.
	Polar Blok B.3	Crystalline metal or Mah. Det. 2LF.	12.	0.	0.	r.
	Polar Blok C.3	ditto HF., Det., LF.	13.	0.	0.	r.
	Polar 4	Mah. Det., 3LF., RC. (Distant tuning control)	32.	10.	0.	r.
	Polar Quartette	Mah. Det., 3LF., RC.	17.	10.	0.	r.
	Polar Blok B.4	Crystalline metal or Mah. Det., 3LF., RC.	16.	0.	0.	r.
	Polar Blok C.4	ditto HF., Det., 2LF, RC.	15.	0.	0.	r.
	Polar Blok D.4	ditto 2HF., Det., LF, RC.	16.	0.	0.	r.
Radio Instruments Limited 12 Hyde Street New Oxford Street London WC1	I.C.	Mah. Crystal Set with lid. 300-500m	2.	2.	0.	r.
	I.D.	ditto 300-500m. and 1600m	2.	15.	0.	r.
	No.209	Mah. Lid and doors. Cryst det., 2LF.	11.	15.	0.	r.
	No.210	Mah. doors. Det., LF.	13.	5.	0.	r.
	Larianette	Mah. doors plus battery cupboard. Det., LF.	20.	8.	0.	r.
	No.211	Mah. doors. Det., 2LF.	16.	17.	6.	r.
	Larianette	Mah. doors plus battery cupboard. Det., 2LF.	25.	9.	6.	r.
	No.1 L.B.	Mah. doors, base. HF., Det., 2LF.	24.	0.	0.	r.
	No.6	Mah. with lid. HF., Det., 2LF.	24.	0.	0.	r.
	No.65A	ditto HF., Det., 3LF.	30.	5.	0.	r.
	No.65	ditto 2HF., Det., 2LF.	30.	5.	0.	r.
	Larian No.4L	Chippendale cabinet. HF., Det., 2LF.	75.	0.	0.	c.

Manufacturer	Equipment name	Description	£	s.	d.	
	Larian No.4L	ditto HF., Det., 3LF.	80.	0.	0.	c.
	Larian No.4L	ditto 2HF., Det., 2LF.	80.	0.	0.	c.
	Larianette	Mah. Portable. Det., LF.	20.	8.	0.	c.
Radio Supply Company Superfone Works Four Oaks Birmingham	Superfone Maxum	Walnut with lid. Crystal set. Variometer.	1.	2.	6.	r.
	Superfone Maxum I	Mah. Portable. One valve set.	4.	17.	6.	r.
	Superfone Maxum II	Mah. Portable. Det., LF., (also table model)	7.	7.	0.	r.
	Superfone Maxim III	Mah. Portable. Det., 2LF, TA.	12.	12.	0.	r.
	Superfone Maxim IV	Mah. Sloping panel. Det., 3LF. TA.	15.	15.	0.	r.
Radio Electric Company 21 St John Street Wolverhampton	R.E.V.B.	Ok. or Mah. Det., LF.	5.	9.	0.	r.
	R.E.3V.B.	Ok. or Mah. Det., 2LF. TC. & RC.	8.	3.	6.	r.
Radio Limited, R.M. 21 Garrick Street London WC2	R.M.10	Ok. or Mah. Det., LF.	11.	11.	0.	r.
	R.M.R. Portable	Leather cased portable set. HF., Det., LF.	19.	19.	0.	c.
	Carpenter	Ok. or Mah. HF., Det., LF.	32.	10.	0.	r.
	R.M.10	Ok. or Mah. Det., 2LF.	14.	10.	0.	r.
Rawle Brothers Stamford Road Handsworth, Birmingham	Fireside	Crystal set in 'Antique' finish.	1.	5.	0.	r.
	Fireside	Ok cabinet. Crystal det., LF.	6.	10.	0.	r.
	Fireside	ditto Crystal det., 2LF.	9.	10.	0.	r.

Maker / Address	Model	Description	£	s.	d.	
Read & Morris Limited, 31 East Castle Street, London W1	Mains set. D.C. Model	Det, LF.	15.	19.	0.	r.
	Mains set. A.C. Model	Det, LF.	20.	3.	0.	r.
	Mains set.	Burr walnut. (made to suit mains supply) Up to:	46.	17.	6.	r.
	Simplicity Five	Mah. sloping panel. 2HF., Det., 2LF. Up to:	73.	3.	0.	r.
	Reamor Portable I	Pigskin attaché. Det., 2LF.	25.	0.	0.	r.
	Reamor Portable II	Pigskin attaché. HF., Det., LF.	25.	0.	0.	r.
Rees, Mace Manufacturing Company Limited	Rees-Mace All-in.	Mah. Portable set. Det., LF.	18.	5.	6.	c.
	ditto	HF., Det., LF.	22.	17.	6.	c.
39a Welbeck Street, London W1	ditto	Det., 2LF.	22.	17.	6.	c.
	ditto	HF., Det., 2LF.	26.	10.	0.	c.
	ditto	2HF., Det., 2LF.	30.	17.	6.	c.
Reeves, A.W. 3 Edmund Street, Birmingham	Reeves-Roberts de Luxe	A four valve set complete with all accessories	30.	0.	0.	c.
	Reeves-Roberts Baby Newt	Imitation leather portable. Reflex neutrodyne.	10.	10.	0.	c.
Rigaut, J. 108 Euston Road, London NW1	L-Type	Mah. closed sloping panel. Crystal set. TI.		19.	6.	r.
	D-Type	Long wave version of above.	1.	2.	6.	r.
	V-Type	Imitation Mah. crystal set. Variometer.		11.	6.	r.

Manufacturer	Equipment name	Description	£	s.	d.	
Rotax (Motor Accessories) Limited Rotax Works Willesden Junction London NW10	Rotola Model A	Black Morocco. Det., LF.	14.	18.	0.	c.
	Rotola Model B	Mah. or Ok. Doors. Det., LF.	14.	18.	0.	c.
	Rotola Portable	Black Morocco. Det., LF.	15.	19.	0.	c.
	Rotola Model A	Mah. Det., 2LF.	28.	2.	6.	c.
	Rotola Model B	Mah., or Ok. Det., 2LF. Self-contained.	33.	7.	6.	c.
	Rotola Model B	Figured walnut. ditto.	34.	7.	6.	c.
Service Radio Company Limited 67 Church Street Stoke Newington London N16	Service	Mah. Lid. Crystal set.	1.	10.	0.	r.
	Service	Mah. Lid. Crystal Det., LF.	3.	0.	0.	r.
	Service	ditto. Crystal Det., 2LF.	4.	0.	0.	r.
S.H.C.S. Company Limited 10 Clare Terrace Sidcup, Kent	Thor No.5	Wal. open Crystal set.		13.	6.	r.
	Thor No.6	Mah. Lid. Crystal set.	1.	7.	6.	r.
	Thor No.8	Mah. Lid. Crystal Det., LF.	6.	15.	0.	r.
	Thor No.9	ditto Crystal Det., 2LF.	14.	14.	0.	c.
	Thor No.10	ditto HF., Det., 2LF.	25.	4.	0.	c.
Sherman, P. 12 River Street London EC1	0.0.	Leather covered crystal set.		15.	0.	r.
	0.	Ok. 'American type' crystal set.	1.	5.	0.	r.
	1.	ditto Crystal Det. Reflex valve. Var.	5.	0.	0.	r.
	6.	ditto with doors. One valve set.	12.	0.	0.	r.
	2.	ditto Det., LF.	7.	15.	0.	r.
	3.	ditto HF., Det., LF.	10.	15.	0.	r.

Maker / Address	Model	Description	£	s.	d.	
	4.	ditto HF., Det., 2LF.	15.	0.	0.	r.
	4A.	Mah. ditto doors HF., Det., 2LF.	20.	0.	0.	r.
	5.	ditto 2HF., Det., 2LF.	30.	0.	0.	r.
	Portable 3.	Ok. HF., Det., LF.	15.	15.	0.	c.
	Portable 4.	Ok. HF., Det., 2LF.	20.	0.	0.	c.
	Portable 5.	Leather. 2HF., Det., 2LF.	30.	0.	0.	c.
Spa Radio Company Limited 107a Locksbrook Road Bath	Spa	Mah. Crystal set.	1.	7.	6.	r.
	Spa	One valve set.	3.	12.	6.	r.
Siemens Brothers & Company Limited Woolwich, London, S.E.18.	Type 125	Mah. Lid. Crystal set.	1.	15.	0.	r.
	Type C.V.	Mah. Lid. Crystal Det., LF.	6.	10.	0.	r.
	S.B.39	Mah. HF., Det., LF.	36.	0.	0.	r.
	M.I.P.	Mah. Portable. HF., Det., LF.	32.	0.	0.	r.
Sterling Telephone & Electric Company Limited.	By 1926 Sterling sets were marketed by Marconiphone. See Marconiphone for listings.					
Stevens & Company Limited, A.J. Walsall Street Wolverhampton	2-valve Standard	Sloping panel. HF., Det.	16.	17.	6.	c.
	3-valve Standard	Sloping panel. HF., Det., LF.	21.	13.	6.	c.
	Console	Mahogany. HF., Det., 2LF.	75.	0.	0.	c.
	Pedestal de Luxe	ditto ditto	65.	0.	0.	c.
	Pedestal	ditto or oak ditto	52.	0.	0.	c.
	Table de Luxe	ditto ditto	35.	0.	0.	c.
	Table	ditto or oak ditto	30.	10.	0.	c.
	4-valve Standard	ditto sloping desk type. ditto	26.	15.	0.	c.

Manufacturer	Equipment name	Description	£	s.	d.	
Stirling Limited 17/19 Clarence Street Kingston-on-Thames Surrey	Stiradio II	Sloping, open panel valves inside. Det., LF.	9.	0.	0.	r.
Stratton & Company Limited Balmoral Works Bromsgrove Street Birmingham	Eddystone Twin	Ok. Lid. Glass front. 2-valves.	15.	15.	0.	c.
Tant & Company, W.H. Transant Works Dollman Street Birmingham	Transant	Ebonite crystal set.	1.	1.	0.	r.
	Transant	Ok. Lid. crystal set.	1.	5.	0.	r.
Telephone Manufacturing Company Limited Hollingsworth Works West Dulwich London SE21	T.M.C.2A	Wood, lid, flat panel crystal set. Slider.	1.	9.	6.	r.
	T.M.C.8	Wal. (or grained ebonite). Sloping panel. Cryst. Var.	2.	7.	6.	r.
	T.M.C.9 Daventry	Moulded case. Crystal set. Variometer.		12.	6.	r.
	T.M.C.2A	Wal. Flat panel. Det., LF.	6.	0.	0.	r.
	T.M.C.7B	Wal. Enclosed. Sloping panel. Glass doors. HF., Det. Rx.	13.	5.	0.	r.
	T.M.C. Trio Portable.	Black leather cloth. 3-valve reflex.	21.	0.	0.	r.

		£	s	d	
T.M.C.4B	Wal. enclosed. Sloping Panel. Glass doors. HF., Det., 2LF.	23.	10.	0.	r.
Terry, Herbert & Sons Limited, Redditch — The Terry	Ok. or Mah. 4-valve set with all accessories	45.	0.	0.	c.
Thames Electric Wireless Company Limited, 40 Old Town, Clapham, London SW4 — Thames	Desk type. Crystal set.	1.	12.	6.	r.
Thames	Panel type. One valve set.	3.	2.	6.	r.
Thames	Panel type. Det., LF.	4.	7.	6.	r.
Thames	Panel type. HF., Det., LF.	11.	0.	0.	r.
Thames	Open Cabinet type. ditto	13.	5.	0.	r.
Thames	Enclosed cabinet type. ditto	14.	10.	0.	r.
Thames	Mah. Seven valve superhet.	32.	14.	6.	r.
Tudoradio Company Limited, Tudor Works, Park Royal, London NW10 — Tudoradio S.B.4.	Mah. or Ok. Doors. (+ Amplion A.R.19) HF., Det., 2LF.	36.	0.	0.	c.
Tutills Limited, 17/9 Swan Street, Manchester — Tinol Electric Main Set.	Ok. Lid. Cryst Det., 2LF. (For D.C. Mains)	13.	10.	0.	r.
Tinol A	Ok. Lid. One valve set.	3.	17.	6.	r.
Tinol Series A	Ok. Lid. Det., LF.	5.	15.	0.	r.
Tinol Series A	Ok. Lid. HF., Det., LF.	8.	5.	0.	r.
Tinol Pure-Tone	Upright. Doors. Det., 2LF. RC.	14.	10.	0.	r.
Tinol Electric Mains Set.	Mah. Double doors. HF., Det., LF. (For D.C. Mains)	26.	10.	0.	c.
ditto	ditto (For A.C. Mains)	28.	10.	0.	c.

Manufacturer	Equipment name	Description	£	Cost s.	d.	
U.S. Radio Company Limited, Radio Works, Tyrwhitt Road, Brockley, London SE4	Yew-ess I	Wal. Open top flat. One valve set.	2.	17.	6.	r.
	Yew-ess II	Open front. Lid. Det., LF.	6.	5.	0.	r.
	Yew-ess II	Ok. Doors with lock for accessories. Det., LF.	8.	10.	0.	r.
	Yew-ess III	ditto Det, 2LF.	7.	17.	6.	r.
Venus Radiophone Company, 1 Percy Street, Fartown, Huddersfield	V.R.I	Ok. or Mah. One valve set.	6.	15	6.	c.
	V.R.II	Ok. or Mah. Det., LF.	13.	10.	0.	c.
	V.R.III	Ok. or Mah. Det., 2LF.	21.	7.	6.	c.
	V.R.IV	Ok. or Mah. HF., Det., 2LF.	28.	5.	6.	c.
	V.R. de Luxe	Jacobean style. HF., Det., 2LF.	35.	0.	0.	c.
	V.R.IV Portable	Leather. HF., Det., 2LF.	25.	10.	0.	c.
	V.R.III Portable	Leather. Det., 2LF.	20.	0.	0.	c.
Ward & Goldstone Limited, Frederick Road, Pendleton, Manchester	Goltone A	Ok. Open type. One valve.	3.	2.	6.	r.
	Goltone	Wooden box crystal set.		7.	6.	r.
	Goltone A	Wooden box, ebonite top. Crystal set.				
	Goltone B	Wooden box, lid, ebonite top. Crystal set.	1.	1.	0.	r.
	Goltone	Wooden case, ebonite top. Crystal Det., LF.	1.	10.	0.	r.
	Goltone A	Ok. case, open type. Det., LF.	7.	7.	6.	c.
	Goltone B	ditto	9.	18.	0.	c.
	Goltone Type A	Ok. Open type. Det., 2LF.	11.	7.	6.	c.
	Goltone Type B	ditto	13.	14.	6.	c.
			15.	1.	6.	c.

Maker / Address	Model	Description	£	s.	d.	
Wates Brothers Limited, 13/14 Great Queen Street, London WC2	Goltone de Luxe	Ok. Cabinet. Det., 2LF.	24.	2.	6.	c.
	Goltone Type A	Ok. Cabinet. HF., Det., 2LF.	16.	10.	0.	c.
	Goltone Type B	ditto	17.	12.	0.	c.
	Goltone de Luxe	Ok. Enclosed cabinet. HF. Det. 2LF.	31.	10.	0.	c.
	Goltone de Luxe	Ok. Enclosed cabinet. HF. Det. 3LF.	37.	12.	6.	c.
	Bijouphone	Tube type, ebonite ends. Crystal set.		10.	0.	r.
Wilkins & Wright Limited, Utility Works, Kenyon Street, Birmingham	Utility	Wooden box crystal set.	2.	2.	0.	r.
Williamson, Robert, 56 Commercial Street, Lerwick, Shetland Islands	Thulephone	Plain cabinet. HF., Det., 2LF.	25.	0.	0.	c.
	Thulephone de Luxe	Cabinet with doors. HF., Det., 2LF.	30.	0.	0.	c.
Wilson & Son Limited, W., 1 London Road, Royston, Hertfordshire	Exceedall	One valve set.	2.	17.	6.	r.
White & Ritchie, 1104 Raeburn Place, Edinburgh	D.S.3 Portable	Ok. cabinet. 3-valve with 2 reflex stages. (2HF, Det., 2LF.)	37.	10.	0.	c.
	Neutrodyne	'American type' 5-valve neutrodyne.	50.	0.	0.	c.

Manufacturer	Equipment name	Description	Cost £	s.	d.	
Wooten Limited, F.E. 56 High Street Oxford	Wootophone Type H2	Mah. Crystal set.	1.	12.	0.	r.
	Wootophone Type E	Mah. or Ok. One valve set.	9.	17.	0.	c.
	Wootophone Type D	Mah. or Ok. Det., LF.	13.	14.	0.	c.
	Wootophone Type C	Mah. or Ok. HF., Det.	15.	14.	0.	c.
	Wootophone Type D2	Mah. or Ok. Det., LF.	12.	0.	0.	c.
	Wootophone Type B	Mah. or Ok. Det., 2LF.	22.	11.	0.	c.
	Wootophone Type A	Mah. or Ok. Four valve set	30.	18.	0.	c.
	Wootophone Type F	Pedestal Type. Four valve set	48.	6.	0.	c.
Yorkshire Radio Company Limited Western Works Rockingham Street Sheffield	Spotter	Enclosed Jacobean. Crystal set. Four versions up to:	1.	5.	0.	r.
	Deucallon	Cabinet. Det., LF.	8.	8.	0.	r.
	Deucallon	Cabinet. HF., Det., 2LF.	31.	10.	0.	r.
Young & Company, A.M. 52 Bordesley Street Birmingham	Rondar	Ok. 'American type' HF., Det.	8.	5.	0.	r.
	Rondar	ditto HF., Det., LF.	12.	0.	0.	r.
	Rondar	ditto HF., Det., 2LF.	15.	10.	0.	r.

Index

Page references followed by the letter f indicate illustrations. Names of journals are in italic and names of people are in heavy type. Company names are included in main index as textual references. Company names are also found under Loudspeaker, Receiver and Valve listings and principally refer to illustrations. Finally, Appendix material is not included in this index.